Published by Pedigree Books under licence from DC Comics.

'NOW YOU SEE'EM' Script & Breakdowns – Steve Vance, Pencils – John Delaney, Inks – Ron Boyd, Letters – Tim Harkins, Colours – Bob LeRose. **'HEADING FOR TROUBLE!'** Script – Steve Vance, Pencils – John Delaney, Inks – Ron Boyd, Letters – Tim Harkins, Colours – Bob LeRose. **'YOU CAN'T CHEETAH AN HONEST MAN'** Script & Breakdowns – Steve Vance, Pencils – John Delaney, Inks – Ron Boyd, Letters – Tim Harkins, Colours – Bob LeRose. **'CRUISE TO NIGHTMARE'** writer – Paul Dini, Artist – Bruce Timm, Colourist – Mark Chiarello, letters – Starkings Comicraft. **'SO THIS LADY WALKS INTO AN ESPRESSO BAR..'** Writer – Steve Vance, Pencils – John Delaney, Inks – Ron Boyd, Letters – Tim Harkins, Colours – Bob LeRose. **'FAMILY MATTERS'** Script – Steve "Sharky" Vance, Pencils – John "Dolphin" Delaney, Inks – Ron "Manta Ray" Boyd, Letters – Tim "Hammerhead" Harkins, Colours – Bob "Barnacle" LeRose.

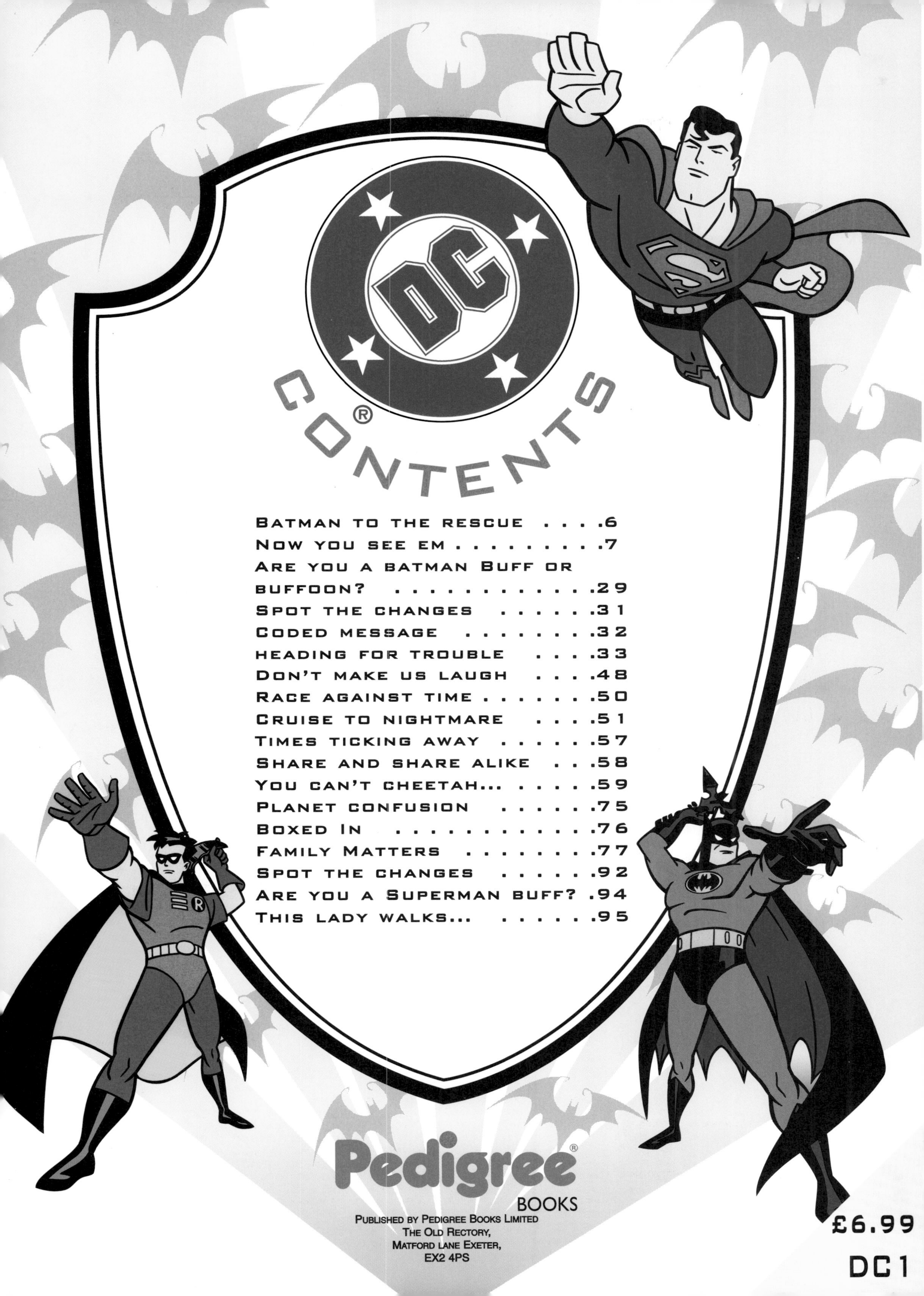

CONTENTS

Pedigree® BOOKS
PUBLISHED BY PEDIGREE BOOKS LIMITED
THE OLD RECTORY,
MATFORD LANE EXETER,
EX2 4PS

£6.99

DC1

BATMAN TO THE RESCUE!

EXAMPLE
11
?
4

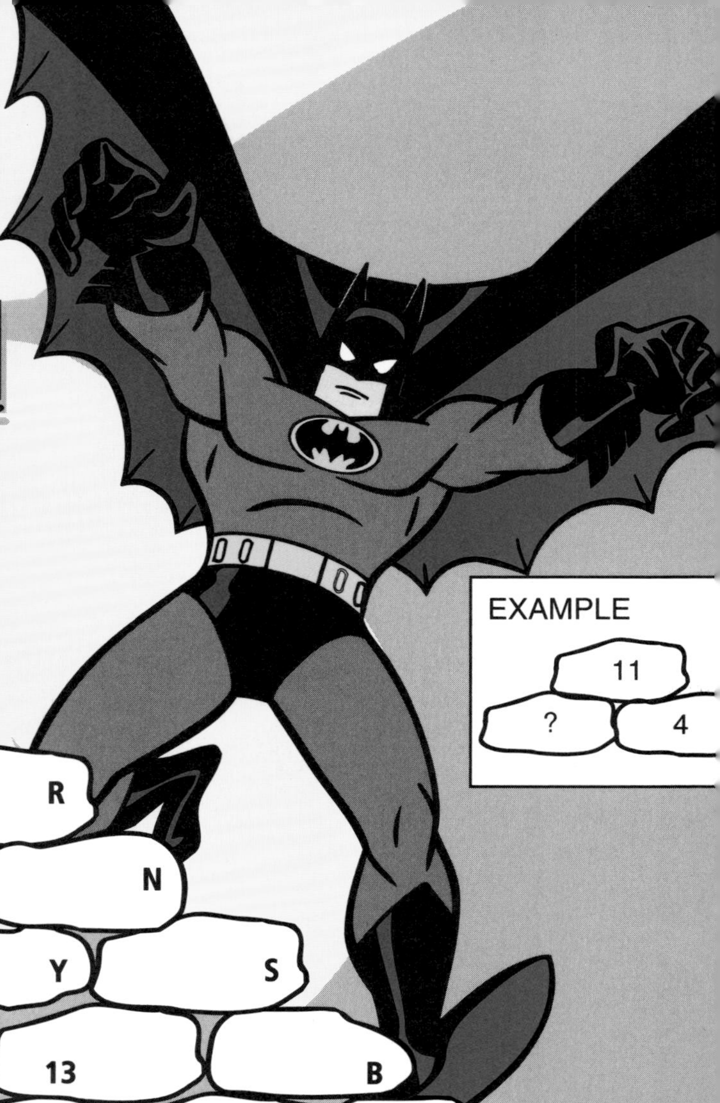

Batman has to get through the pile of boulders to rescue Robin, who is being held hostage! First trace this page on to paper. Then solve the puzzle to smash the boulders!

The number in each boulder is the sum of the two numbers beneath. So in the example, the question mark should be a 7. Write the correct numbers in the pyramid, then transfer the letters to the boxes to see a joke!

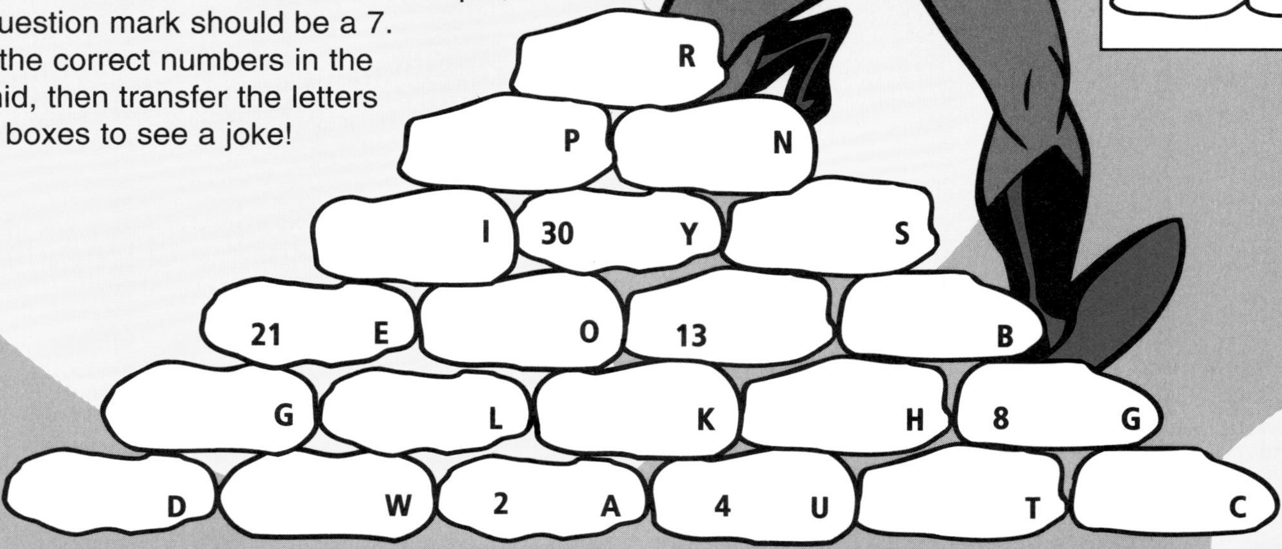

R
P
N
I
30
Y
S
21
E
O
13
B
G
L
K
H
8
G
D
W
2
A
4
U
T
C

9 7 38 5 7   15 38 126 1   10 126 17 9 28   4 68

9 7 38 11 21   38 3   10 126 17 9 28   1 17 9 58 ?

2   15 2 15 30   1 4 5 6 11 38 58 8 .

Answers:

126
68
58
38
30
28
21
17
13
15
10
11
6
7
8
1
9
2
4
3
5

Answers:

Which Bird Grows Up
While It Grows Down?
A Baby Duckling.

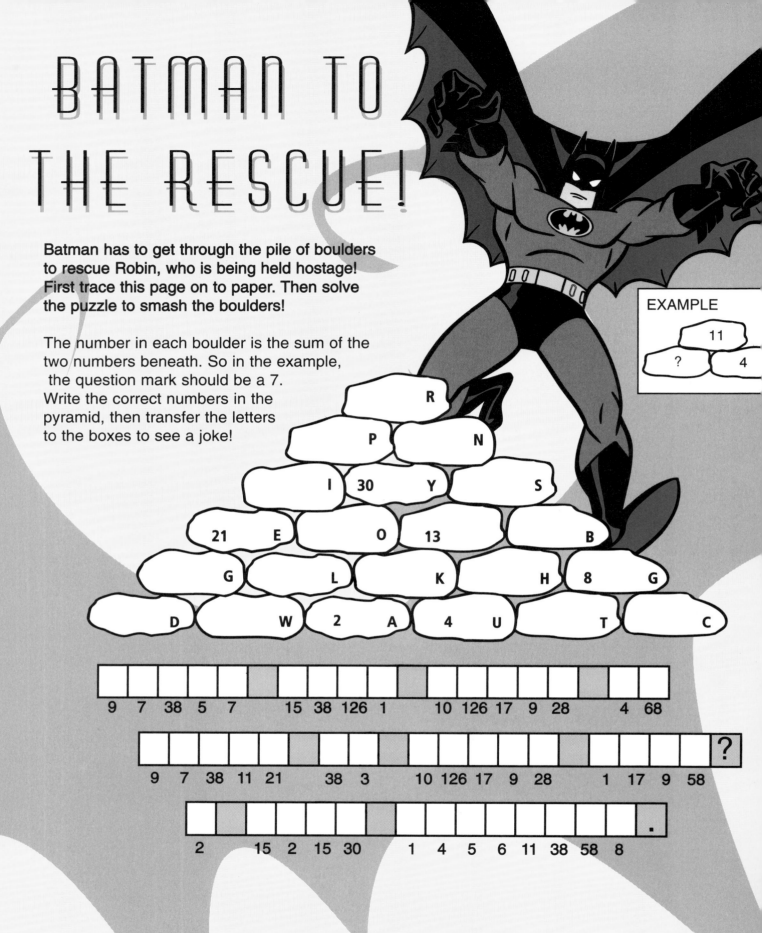

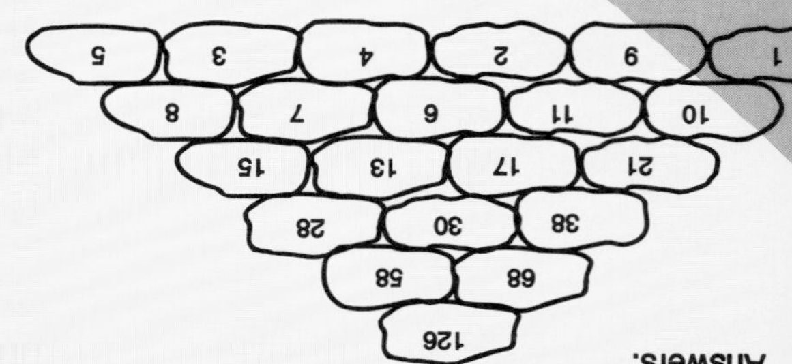

STOP, FLASH--
OR HE DIES!!
THE JUSTICE LEAGUE OF AMERICA IN
NOW YOU SEE 'EM...
STEVE VANCE - SCRIPT + BREAKDOWNS
JOHN DELANEY - PENCILS
RON BOYD - INKS
TIM HARKINS - LETTERS
BOB LE ROSE - COLORS
FRANK BERRIOS - ASS'T EDITS
KC CARLSON - EDITS
LIVE
WKEY
LINDA PARK WKEY
THIS IS LINDA PARK REPORTING LIVE FROM THE NEW KEYSTONE TOWER, WHERE THE FLASH IS BATTLING GORILLA GRODD!
IT ALL BEGAN DURING THE DEDICATION CEREMONIES FOR THE TOWER--

"-- JUST MINUTES AGO!"
REMIND ME AGAIN WHY WE'RE HERE.
YOU'RE HERE FOR THE FREE CHAMPAGNE, WALLY. I'M HERE BECAUSE THE MAN WHO BUILT THIS TOWER WANTS TO BUY A MEDIA EMPIRE TO GO ALONG WITH IT --
WKEY

-- INCLUDING WKEY. HE MAY BE MY NEW BOSS SOON, SO I HAVE TO PRETEND HE'S NEWSWORTHY.
LADIES AND GENTLEMEN--
GOTTA GO! THERE HE IS NOW--

--MR. WINSTON "WINNER" MCKINNEY!
EVER SINCE I SOLD McKINNEY INDUSTRIES' ARMAMENTS DIVISION, I'VE BEEN LOOKING FOR A NEW WAY TO SERVE THE PUBLIC.
THAT'S WHY I BUILT KEYSTONE TOWER-- TO BE THE CORNERSTONE OF A NEW BROADCAST SERVICE.

BY THROWING THIS SWITCH TO POWER UP OUR ANTENNA ARRAY, McKINNEY INDUSTRIES IS, SO TO SPEAK, BEATING ITS SWORDS INTO RATINGS SHARES!

YAY! CLAP!
VZZAK!
CLAP! HOORAY!
CLAP!

... SPEAKING WITH GADSDEN GRAVES, WHO HELPED WINSTON McKINNEY START HIS FIRST ENGINEERING FIRM WHILE THEY WERE BOTH STILL IN HIGH SCHOOL.
I HEAR YOU'RE THE BRAINS OF THE OPERATION. WHY ISN'T IT McKINNEY-GRAVES INDUSTRIES?
UH, I UH, GUESS I'M MORE THE, UH, BEHIND-THE-SCENES TYPE, MS. PARK.
WKEY

AS THE FIRM'S CHIEF FINANCIAL OFFICER, COULD YOU TELL ME --
THERE YOU ARE!

I WANT TO MAKE A TOAST TO OUR NEW ENDEAVOR, BUT I CAN'T FIND MY-- SAY, YOU HAVEN'T TOUCHED YOUR DRINK, GAD--
--ALLOW ME!

LINDA! WHAT A PLEASURE. I'VE BEEN TOLD THAT YOU ARE ONE OF WKEY'S GREATEST ASSETS. I LOOK FORWARD TO WORKING CLOSELY WITH YOU...
...VERY CLOSELY.

THAT'S ENOUGH, WIN!

I'M-I'M SICK OF YOU TREATING EVERYONE LIKE SERVANTS... OR WORSE!

DING!

WHERE D'YA THINK YOU'RE GOING, PAL?
WAIT! I-I'M--

KA-BUDDA-BUDDA!
KABLAM!
GUNSHOTS--FROM THE CORRIDOR! BUT WHO--?

TAKE IT EASY, FOLKS--IT'LL BE A LOT LESS FATAL FOR YA! WE'RE HERE FOR ONE THING--
--WINSTON McKINNEY!

KRRRAAASH!
GAAAAH!
WELL DONE, MY MINIONS! NOW SEE TO THE GUESTS--
--WHILE McKINNEY AND I HAVE A PRIVATE CONFERENCE!
IT'S SUPER-GORILLA GRODD!
THANKS, BUT
I DIDN'T THINK
IT WAS
HARRY THE HYPER-HAMSTER!
IN THE BLINK OF AN EYE, WALLY WEST DONS THE COSTUME OF THE FASTEST MAN ALIVE--
THE FLASH
AAH--AHH --AAH!
STOP SQUIRMING, LITTLE MAN-- UNLESS YOU WANT ME TO DROP YOU!
NOT SO FAST, GRODD!

FLASH!
THE DAY PAYS DIVIDENDS! NOT ONLY DO I GET THE IDEAL PLATFORM FROM WHICH TO BROADCAST MY MIND-CONTROL BEAMS--
--I ALSO GET TO DESTROY YOU!

STOP, FLASH--OR HE DIES!
YOU'RE

KIDDING,

RIGHT?

I- I--
AAIIIEEEE!
GUESS I'D BETTER GO CATCH GRODD--

--BEFORE HE
MAKES A
BIG SPLAT ON THE--
huh? WHERE'D HE GO?

...COPS SAY GRODD'S MEN DON'T KNOW *HOW* HE ESCAPED, WALLY.
THOSE GOONS DIDN'T PUT UP MUCH OF A FIGHT--THEY SEEMED AS SURPRISED AS I WAS!
GRODD HAS SOME DANGEROUS POWERS, BUT I NEVER KNEW HE COULD JUST--

--*VANISH INTO THIN AIR?!*
DENVER:
SO YOU'VE CHOSEN TO *FLEE*, MANHUNTER? IT'S A WISE MAN--OR, IN THIS CASE, MARTIAN--WHO KNOWS WHEN HE'S BEATEN!

AND NOW, BACK TO THE BUSINESS AT HAND--

--POCKET CHANGE WORTH *MILLIONS*--AND I HAVE *VERY LARGE POCKETS!*

GOLD RUSH

YOU'LL NOT FILL THEM HERE, ***BLOCKBUSTER!***

BASH!

WHAOOOF!

SO--YOU CAN RENDER YOURSELF INVISIBLE! YOU'LL WISH YOU HAD FLED! SHOW YOURSELF, COWARD!
VERY WELL...

...THOUGH IT WILL AVAIL YOU LITTLE.
YOU TREACHEROUS ALIEN--!
LONG AGO, ON MARS, HE WAS NAMED J'ONN J'ONZZ--BUT ON HIS ADOPTED HOME PLANET, MEN CALL HIM
MARTIAN MANHUNTER

YOU HAVE DONE TOO MUCH DAMAGE ALREADY--BUT BY MEANS OF THE TUNNEL YOU DUG, I CAN TAKE YOU AWAY AND PREVENT FURTHER DESTRUCTION.

SURELY YOU DIDN'T THINK YOU COULD LOOT THE U.S. MINT UNNOTICED!
ON THE CONTRARY--I WAS COUNTING ON DRAWING YOUR ATTENTION...

THWAKOOMPF!
...SO I COULD SMASH YOU!

SPOKK!

THONK!
KRAAAASH!
THAT SMELL --GAS!
BLAST.

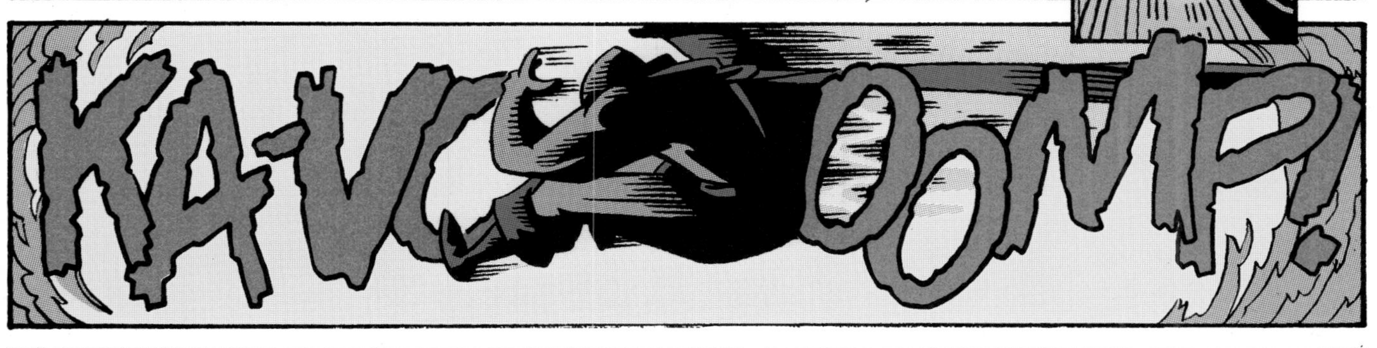
KA-VOOOMP!

I MUST BATTLE MY FEAR OF FIRE--AND RESCUE BLOCKBUSTER FROM THE HEART OF THE FLAMES!
IF I CAN DOUSE THE BLAZE WITH THIS WATER MAIN...

THERE IS NO TRACE OF HIM. BUT HOW--?

OFF THE CALIFORNIA COAST:

...BUT HOW CAN SUCH A THING HAPPEN?

IT WAS THE STRANGEST SERIES OF FLUKES YOU EVER HEARD OF-- A FAULTY WARNING LIGHT, A CREWMAN WITH THE FLU, A STRAY TRAWLER, AND THEN THIS ROTTEN WEATHER.

MINOR PROBLEMS INDIVIDUALLY, BUT ALL TOGETHER--

"--THEY SANK A NUCLEAR SUBMARINE!"

"THE CREW ESCAPED, BUT IF THE SUB SLIPS OFF THOSE ROCKS AND SINKS DEEPER, THE PRESSURE WILL CRUSH ITS HULL LIKE--"

SPARE ME YOUR CLICHÉS, CAPTAIN. I KNOW THE DANGER POSED BY A *LEAKING NUCLEAR REACTOR*.

I ONLY WISH YOU *SURFACE-DWELLERS* UNDERSTOOD IT AS WELL.

HE SLIPS BENEATH THE WAVES WITH EASE, FOR THE SEVEN SEAS ARE HIS KINGDOM. HE IS

AQUAMAN

WISH I COULD IGNORE THIS-- MAKE THEM LEARN TO DEAL WITH THEIR OWN PROBLEMS--

-- BUT THE RISK IS TOO *GREAT*, AND THE PLANET TOO *SMALL*.

WHAT'S THAT--?

"--THE NAVY SAID IT HAD NO MINI-SUBS IN THE AREA!"
PERFECT! THE HOLE CAUSED BY THE COLLISION WITH THE TRAWLER GIVES ME ACCESS TO THE SUB'S *NUCLEAR MISSILES!*

AND THE SHIFT IN WEIGHT CAUSED BY THE REMOVAL OF THE MISSILES WILL DISLODGE THE SUB AND SEND IT TO A WATERY GRAVE-- JUST AS I CALCULATED!
ANOTHER TRIUMPH FOR *MAJOR DISASTER!*

SHA-MOOO!
YAAAAH!

AQUAMAN! I THOUGHT HE WAS 10,000 MILES AWAY! WELL, HE'LL HAVE TO CHOOSE BETWEEN CAPTURING ME...

...AND PREVENTING A NUCLEAR CATASTROPHE!
KRUMBLE!

WRONG, MAJOR! MY FRIENDS WILL TAKE CARE OF THE SUB--

--WHILE I TAKE CARE OF YOU!
SKREEK!

GONE!?
I'LL TELEPATHICALLY CHECK WITH FISH IN THE VICINITY--BUT SOMETHING TELLS ME WE WON'T FIND HIM!

METROPOLIS:
THOOOM!
THOUGH HE MAY NOT LOOK IT RIGHT NOW, THE GUY WITH THE "S" ON HIS CHEST IS EARTH'S GREATEST CHAMPION--
SUPERMAN
RUN, SUPERMAN! RUN FROM THE DEADLY TOUCH OF THE PARASITE!

YOU CAN'T ESCAPE ME! I'LL HUNT YOU DOWN AND DRAIN YOU DRY! YOUR POWER WILL BE MI--

WHAT!? WHO--?

--OOOH.

CHUMPF!

THE SCRAP HEAP DOWN AT THE SHIPYARDS SURE COMES IN HANDY SOMETIMES.
NOW TO GET PARASITE BACK INSIDE A NULL-ENERGY CONTAINMENT FIELD--

HOW ON EARTH--? HE'S VANISHED!

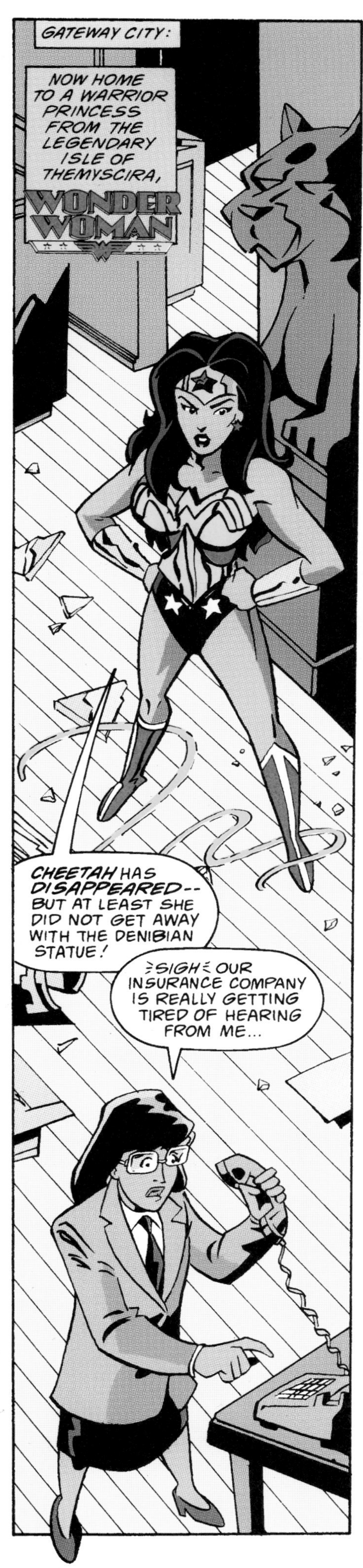
GATEWAY CITY:
NOW HOME TO A WARRIOR PRINCESS FROM THE LEGENDARY ISLE OF THEMYSCIRA,
WONDER WOMAN
CHEETAH HAS DISAPPEARED-- BUT AT LEAST SHE DID NOT GET AWAY WITH THE DENIBIAN STATUE!
≥SIGH≤ OUR INSURANCE COMPANY IS REALLY GETTING TIRED OF HEARING FROM ME...

NEW YORK.
HE WIELDS THE POWER RING, PERHAPS THE GREATEST WEAPON EVER DEVISED. HE IS
GREEN LANTERN
... AND HE IS FRUSTRATED!
RATS! I FINALLY GET DR. LIGHT ON THE ROPES-- AND HE MANAGES TO PULL A HOUDINI ON ME!

GOTHAM CITY:
THE DARK KNIGHT. THE WORLD'S GREATEST DETECTIVE. THIS IS HIS TURF. HE'S
BATMAN
AT LEAST WE STOPPED THE SCARECROW'S FEAR GAS-- BUT HOW DID HE ESCAPE? MY MEN HAD THE WHOLE BLOCK SURROUNDED!
HMMM...

THE MOON.
A LONG COMMUTE, BUT WORTH IT FOR THE VIEW. HEADQUARTERS FOR THE BAND OF HEROES KNOWN AS THE
JLA
THANKS FOR COMING. JUDGING FROM NEWS REPORTS, WE'VE ALL ENCOUNTERED A SIMILAR PHENOMENON TODAY...

... SO I THOUGHT IT MIGHT BE A GOOD IDEA TO COMPARE NOTES ON OUR DISAPPEARING FOES.
AGREED.
YEAH! IF TWICE IS A COINCIDENCE AND THREE TIMES IS A PATTERN--
--THEN SEVEN TIMES PROBABLY MEANS A HEAVY-DUTY SUPER-VILLAIN CONSPIRACY!
BUT WHERE DO WE START?
I'VE GOT SOMETHING.

GEEZ, WHAT TOOK YOU SO LONG?
UH, JUST KIDDING, BATMAN.

I HYPOTHESIZED THAT OUR FOES VANISHED BY MEANS OF SOME TYPE OF TRANSPORTER DEVICE.
I CORRELATED SPIKES IN ELECTRICAL USAGE WITH THE TIMING OF THE EVENTS...
...CHECKED FOR ANOMALOUS COMMUNICATIONS SATELLITE TRANSMISSIONS...

...AND CAME UP WITH THIS.
SO, IN PLAIN ENGLISH--THAT'S WHERE THE BAD GUYS ARE. WHAT ARE WE WAITING FOR?

BENEATH THE SOUTHWESTERN DESERT:
(WHERE THE BAD GUYS ARE.)
HAD FLASH RIGHT WHERE I WANTED HIM, BUT MY IDIOTIC HENCHMEN--
THAT'S WHERE YOU WENT WRONG-- DR. LIGHT DOESN'T RELY ON UNDERLINGS.
RELIABLE INFORMATION THAT AQUAMAN WAS IN THE SOUTH ATLANTIC!
BAH! MY INFORMANTS FAILED TO TELL ME THE FULL RANGE OF MY OPPONENT'S POWERS!
GRRRR!
OF ALL THE ROTTEN LUCK...
BUT NEXT TIME.
IN OTHER WORDS--

--YOU ALL FAILED.
A PITY... BUT I RECOGNIZED THE RISKS WHEN I BANKROLLED YOUR ENDEAVORS.
WHO ARE YOU TO CRITICIZE US?! WE TOOK ALL THE RISKS!
YOU'RE A BLANK--A CIPHER! WE DON'T EVEN KNOW YOUR NAME!

YOU MAY CALL ME "CIPHER" IF IT WILL SALVE YOUR WOUNDED PRIDE, BLOCKBUSTER.
NOW, IF YOU'LL ALL RETURN THE TELEPORT SIGNAL-LOCK DEVICES YOU'VE BEEN WEARING...
MUTTER MUTTER GRUMBLE GRUMBLE
WHAT NOW? PLAN A NEW CAPER?
HOW ABOUT "SURRENDER PEACEFULLY"?

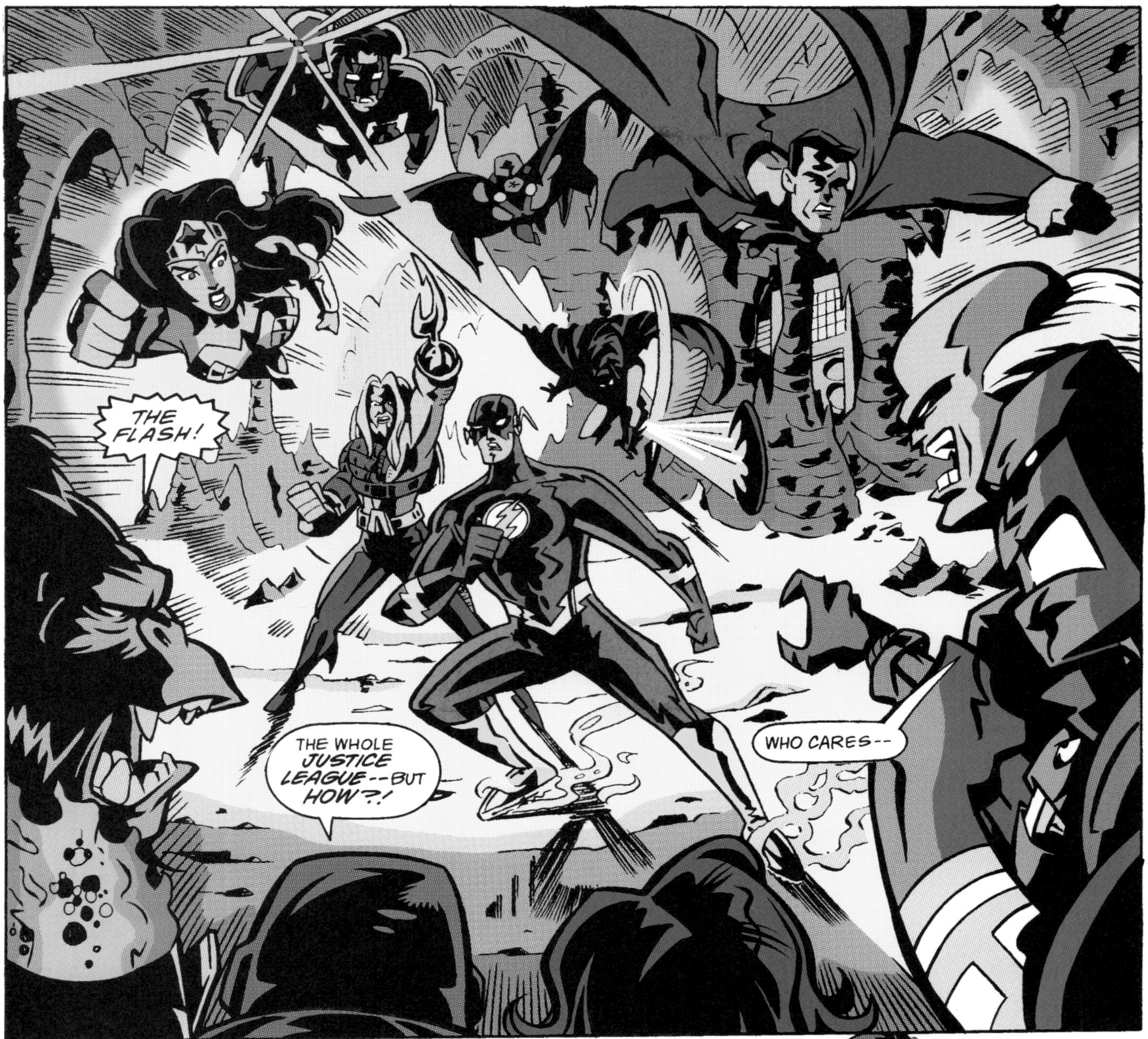

THE FLASH!

THE WHOLE JUSTICE LEAGUE--BUT HOW?!

WHO CARES--

THOK!
VRR
CHNK
CHINK!
RRROOWWWL

WHRRR! CHIK!
KLANK! CHIK!
KRRRUNCHH!
CHUD!
GGH!

RRRR!

NOW, JUSTICE LEAGUE--
KRA-CHUNK!
--I OFFER YOU THE CHANCE TO SURRENDER PEACEFULLY!
WHAT THE--? A ROBOT?!
NO, A BATTLE-SUIT, WITH A HUMAN OPERATOR INSIDE--PROBABLY THE BRAINS BEHIND ALL THIS!
MUST BE LINED WITH LEAD--MY X-RAY VISION WON'T PENETRATE IT!
IT IS EQUALLY IMPERVIOUS TO MY MENTAL PROBES!
YEAH, YEAH--"RESISTANCE IS FUTILE"--

--DON'T THESE GUYS KNOW WE EAT BATTLESUITS FOR BREAKFAAAH!
ZZIKK!

UNNNH... A KRYPTONITE-POWERED BLASTER!
FWOOOSH
FIRE! NO!

WHOA! THE BIG BOYS ARE DOWN!
DISTRACT HIM, FLASH. AQUAMAN, WONDER WOMAN --FOLLOW MY LEAD.

THAT'S RIGHT, ROBO-BOY-- TRY AND CATCH ME!

SPA-THONK!
KRA-CHONK!
ZZZAK!

I THINK IT'S TIME WE FOUND OUT WHO'S INSIDE THAT TIN CAN, DON'T YOU?
INDEED!

OKAY, WHOEVER YOU ARE! TIME TO--
HUH?!
SKRRUNCH!

HE MUST HAVE TELEPORTED AWAY! THE SUIT IS EMPTY!
NOT QUITE!
CLEAR OUT, EVERYONE! THERE'S A BOMB!
TIKTIKTIKTIKTIKTIKTIK

KAVOOOOOOOOM!

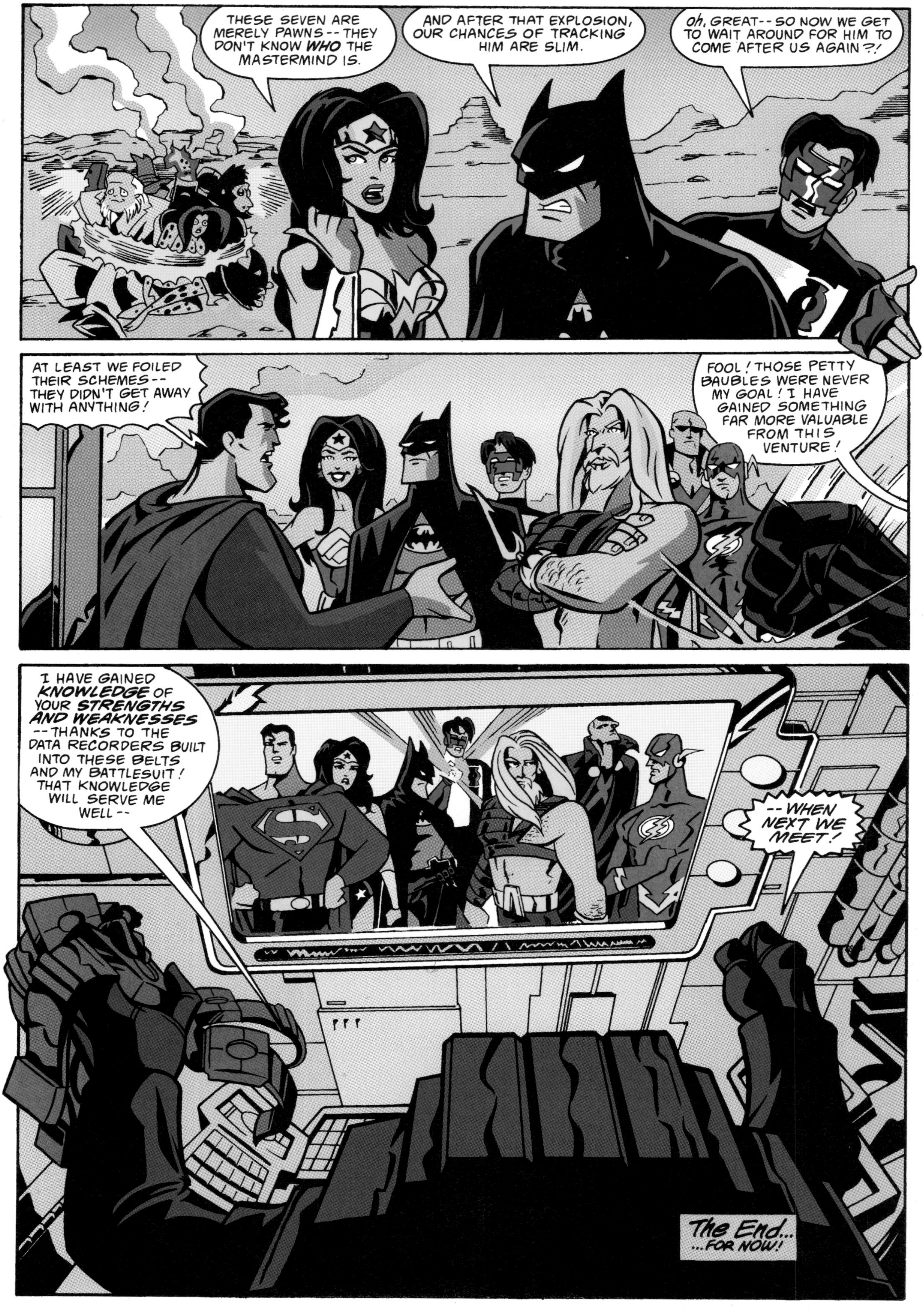

I HAVE GAINED **KNOWLEDGE** OF YOUR **STRENGTHS AND WEAKNESSES** -- THANKS TO THE DATA RECORDERS BUILT INTO THESE BELTS AND MY BATTLESUIT! THAT KNOWLEDGE WILL SERVE ME WELL --

-- **WHEN NEXT WE MEET!**

The End... ...FOR NOW!

ARE YOU A BATMAN BUFF... OR BUFFOON?

So you think you know everything there is to know about the Caped Crusaders, huh! Answer these questions, then check your score to see if you're really such a big Batman bod!

Q1 Where do Batman and Robin live?
A. Gotham Town
B. Gresham City
C. Gotham City

Q2 The Riddler's original name was:
A. Freddie Nuston
B. Eddie Nashton
C. Eddie Cashon

Q3 Batman and Robin have an arch-enemy called:
A. The Penguin
B. The Owl
C. The Pelican

Q4 Batman's real name is:
A. Boris West
B. Bruce West
C. Bruce Wayne

Q5 Who's the 'funny' crook who tries to outwit our two heroes?
A. The Jester
B. The Joker
C. The Jouster

Q6 What colour is the Batmobile?
A. black
B. orange
C. green

Q7 Bruce Wayne's butler is called:
A. Albert
B. Alex
C. Alfred

Q8 Which evil crook tries to keep Batman and Robin in the cold?
A. Mr. Icicle
B. Mr. Freeze
C. Mr. Chill

Q9 Name the Police Commissioner in Gotham City
A. Gordon
B. Golden
C. Garden

Q10 Batman and Robin use their super-human powers
A. All the time
B. Never
C. When their enemies use super-human powers

SCORE: 0-6 points
Have you actualy ever heard of Batman and robin? we don't think so!

SCORE: 8-14 points
Not bad...but you need to read up a bit more on our Caped Crusaders!

SCORE: 16-20 points
Well done! You're obviously a big Batman and Robin fan!

SCORE: over 20 points
You really do know everything about the Caped Crusaders! You even got the trick question right!

Answer:
Give yourself 2 points for every correct answer.
1-C. 2-B. 3-A. 4-C. 5-B. 6-A. 7-C. 8-B. 9-A. 10-B (This was a trick question, because Batman and Robin don't have super-human powers!) If you answered this one correctly, score '5' points!

SPOT THE DIFFERENCE
Superman's arrived just in time to stop another evil enemy from taking over the city! Say how picture 'B' is different to 'A' in twelve ways!
A

Answer:
Twelve things are missing from 'B': The line in Superman's cape on his left shoulder; a skyscraper; one window from the tall skyscraper; one window from the middle building; the lamp-post; one cloud by the tallest skyscraper; one cloud by the door; two pieces of rock; a building support; rubbish bin lid and an oval light.

CRACK THE CODE

Superman has been sent a message – but what does it say? Can you crack the code and tell Superman where he needs to be?

Answer:
The coded message reads:
Jimmy Olsen is trapped inside the Daily Planet.

ARROGANCE! THAT'S WHAT I HATE ABOUT THESE COSTUMED FOOLS!
THEY CALL THEMSELVES "SUPERHEROES!" THEY THINK THEY'RE BETTER THAN EVERYONE ELSE!

BIG EGOS-- BIG HEADS--
--AND THE FLASH IS THE WORST!

HE DOESN'T EVEN CONCEAL HIS IDENTITY! HE LIVES FOR THE ADULATION OF AN IDIOT PUBLIC!
SOON HE'LL REALIZE WHAT A MISTAKE THAT IS--

--A FATAL MISTAKE!

HEADING FOR TROUBLE!

KRRRUNCH!

STEVE VANCE · SCRIPT JOHN DELANEY · PENCILS RON BOYD · INKS TIM HARKINS · LETTERS
BOB LEROSE · COLORS · FRANK BERRIOS · ASS'T EDITS KC CARLSON · HEAD HONCHO

BLAST! THAT'S THE THIRD ONE THIS MONTH.
BZZZT
BRING ME ANOTHER FLASH ACTION FIGURE --IMMEDIATELY!
YESSIR! RIGHT AWAY!
I SHARE YOUR VIEWS REGARDING FLASH, OF COURSE -- BUT SUCCESS REQUIRES MORE THAN UNITY OF PURPOSE!
WHAT IS YOUR PLAN?
A WELL-TESTED ONE, GRODD.
YOU KNOW THE TRICKSTER, OF COURSE.
OF COURSE. BUT TELL ME, CIPHER--WHY SHOULD I CARE ABOUT THAT PETTY CROOK?
"BECAUSE, SOME YEARS AGO, HE BUILT A DEVICE THAT NEARLY KILLED WALLY WEST'S PREDECESSOR."
"FIRED AT THE PREVIOUS FLASH, IT CAUSED HIS HEAD TO SWELL DANGEROUSLY--"
"--BUT THE TRICKSTER'S MISTAKES ALLOWED THE FLASH TO REVERSE THE EFFECTS AND SAVE HIMSELF.
NOW THE TRICKSTER HAS GONE STRAIGHT--AND I HAVE ACQUIRED THE DEVICE FROM A DISGRUNTLED FORMER UNDERLING OF HIS.
I HAVE REENGINEERED THE WEAPON--MAKING ITS RAYS BOTH INVISIBLE AND MORE LETHAL!
AND HOW DO YOU PROPOSE TO EMPLOY IT? SIMPLY KNOCK ON WEST'S DOOR AND--
FLASH TRAVELS FREQUENTLY BETWEEN KEYSTONE CITY AND SANTA MARTA--AND I HAVE MAPPED HIS USUAL ROUTE!
HE GOES THROUGH THIS REMOTE MOUNTAIN PASS ALMOST EVERY DAY.
HMM... AN AMBUSH. INTRIGUING.
HERE'S THE FIGURE YOU ASKED FOR, SIR.
VERY WELL-- NOW LEAVE US.

GOOD THING WE LAID IN A BIG SUPPLY OF THOSE DOLLS, THE WAY HE GOES THROUGH 'EM.
SO WHAT'S IT LIKE WORKING FOR THIS GUY CIPHER?
I'VE ONLY BEEN HERE A COUPLE WEEKS. PRETTY QUIET SO FAR.

IT'S ALWAYS LIKE THAT BETWEEN JOBS-- BUT YOU GOTTA STAY ALERT. GRODD GOES INTA ACTION WHEN YOU LEAST EXPECT IT.
I WORKED FOR MAJOR DISASTER ONCE-- TOTALLY DIFFERENT STORY. HE PLANNED EVERYTHING MONTHS IN ADVANCE.
IF YOU WERE TWO SECONDS LATE, HE FIRED YOU. BUT HE OFFERED A GREAT RETIREMENT PLAN--AND BOY, COULD HE PICK STOCKS.

WHAT'S WITH THOSE TWO, ANYWAY? WHY MAKE IT SO COMPLICATED? YOU WANNA KILL FLASH, GRAB A GUN AND START BLASTING.!
I ASKED GRODD ONE TIME. HE SAID IT WAS LIKE ASKING MICHELANGELO WHY HE DIDN'T USE A ROLLER TO PAINT THE SISTINE CHAPEL.

"WHAT DOES THAT MEAN?"
"BEATS ME."
I AM CURIOUS, CIPHER--IF THIS PLAN IS FOOLPROOF, WHY GIVE IT TO ME?
I'M DOING YOU A FAVOR, GRODD-- AND I'LL EXPECT YOU TO RETURN THAT FAVOR WHEN I ASK.
BESIDES, I AM MORE COMFORTABLE OPERATING BEHIND THE SCENES.

I SEE.
GIVEN THE DISMAL FAILURE OF OUR LAST JOINT VENTURE*, I HAVE NO WISH TO BE BEHOLDEN TO YOU IN THE FUTURE.
I'LL PASS.
...BUT I CAN ALWAYS IMPLEMENT PART OF THIS PLAN ON MY OWN!
*BACK IN ISSUE #1 -KC

YOU'LL REGRET THIS, GRODD!
AND A GOOD DAY TO YOU, TOO, CIPHER.
COME ALONG, YOU LAZY WRETCHES!

BLAST!
XRRRUNCH!
BRING ME ANOTHER GRODD ACTION FIGURE IMMEDIATELY!
YESSIR!
IN FACT, BRING SEVERAL!
YESSIR!

FINALLY-- THE END OF ANOTHER DAY OF SUN-DRENCHED SUPERHEROING ON THE LEFT COAST.
CALIFORNIA'S A NICE PLACE TO WORK, BUT CALL ME WALLY MID-WEST -- I WOULDN'T WANT TO LIVE OUT THERE.
...AND, THANKS TO MY FLASHING FEET, I DON'T HAVE TO! MY THOUSAND-MILE-PLUS COMMUTE ONLY TAKES A FEW MINUTES--
--AND THAT'S IF I SLOW DOWN TO ENJOY THE SCENERY!
THE ROCKIES AT SUNSET! MY FAVORITE PART OF THE TRIP--
--NEXT TO SEEING LINDA WHEN I GET HOME!
HE'LL BE HERE IN SECONDS! EVERYTHING IS IN READINESS!
I SUPPOSE I SHOULD HAVE KNOWN--IF YOU WANT SOMETHING DONE RIGHT--
HERE COMES FLASH-- AND NO SIGN OF CIPHER! I MUST REMEMBER TO THANK HIM WHEN NEXT WE MEET--
--THOUGH HE MERELY PROVIDED THE OPPORTUNITY! THE KEY TO THIS PLAN--
--DO IT YOURSELF!
--IS MY DEVOLUTION RAY!

THIS IS IT--THE BEGINNING OF THE END OF THE FLASH--
--AND HE'LL NEVER KNOW WHAT HIT HIM!

SOON, FLASH WILL DEVOLVE TO A PRIMITIVE STATE! THEN I CAN EASILY CONTROL HIS MIND--
--OR SIMPLY CRUSH HIM!
STRANGE--
I FELT A LITTLE DIZZY THERE FOR A MOMENT.
GUESS I SHOULDN'T HAVE SKIPPED LUNCH.
BY TOMORROW MORNING, FLASH'S HEAD WILL EXPLODE--
--AND I WILL FINALLY CLAIM MY FIRST VICTIM!

ahhh--FOR ONCE, I'M HOME AT A REASONABLE HOUR! NOW--

--IF WALLY WOULD ONLY SHOW UP SOON, WE COULD HAVE A NICE, QUIET DINNER AT HOME...
...IF THERE'S ANYTHING IN HERE THAT DOESN'T REQUIRE CARBON DATING!
Oh, WELL -- THERE'S ALWAYS TAKE-OUT.

KLIK!
WALLY! IS THAT--
--YOU?

WALLY!

WHAT'S HAPPENED TO YOU?
I AM UNCERTAIN. HOWEVER--

--I INTEND TO ELUCIDATE THE SITUATION!
huh? "ELUCIDATE THE--"?
WALLY?!

MY GOSH! HE'S TURNING OUR LIVING ROOM INTO AN INSTANT LABORATORY!
WALLY--SHOULDN'T YOU CALL S.T.A.R. LABS? YOU'RE NOT A SCIENTIST!
--THOUGH YOU CERTAINLY ARE SOUNDING LIKE ONE!
YOUR TREPIDATION IS UNWARRANTED, LINDA--
--MY INTELLECT HAS ENLARGED--
--IN PROPORTION TO MY CRANIUM!

WALLY! ARE YOU OKAY?
APART FROM >huff< THE DISTENSION OF MY CEREBRUM, YOU MEAN? ->puff<-
I WOULD HYPOTHESIZE ->huff<- THIS HYPERACTIVITY ->puff<- HAS CAUSED MY FATIGUE!

I'M AFRAID THERE'S MORE TO IT THAN THAT! ORDINARILY, YOU WOULD HAVE DONE ALL THIS WITHOUT BREAKING A SWEAT!
LET US HOPE THE TESTS I HAVE INITIATED PROVIDE THE ANSWERS.

EUREKA! I HAVE FOUND IT!
AND JUST IN TIME -- MY HEAD IS THREATENING TO BURST!

IN BETWEEN EXPERIMENTS, I HAVE BEEN REVIEWING BARRY ALLEN'S CASE FILES.
I THOUGHT PERHAPS HE HAD ENCOUNTERED SOMETHING SIMILAR WHEN HE WAS THE FLASH--

--AND I WAS CORRECT!

FOLLOWING HIS NOTES, I CAN CONSTRUCT A DEVICE --
--THAT SHOULD INSTANTLY REVERSE THE EFFECTS OF THE TRICKSTER'S RAY!

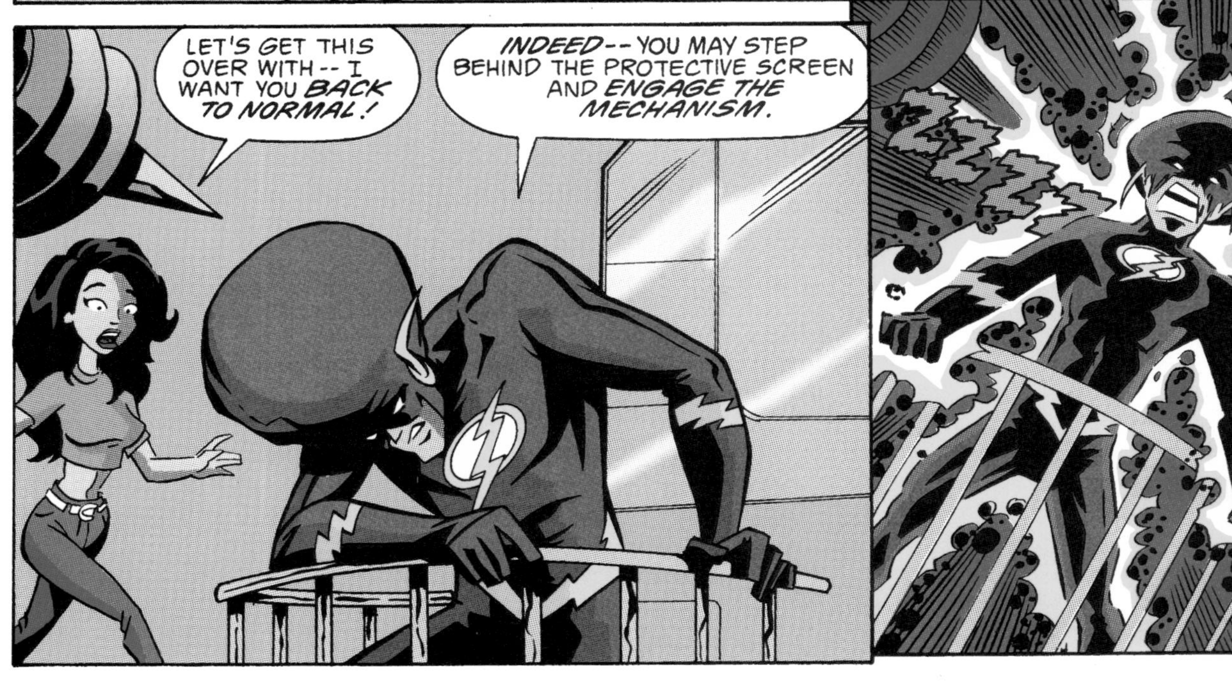
LET'S GET THIS OVER WITH -- I WANT YOU BACK TO NORMAL!
INDEED-- YOU MAY STEP BEHIND THE PROTECTIVE SCREEN AND ENGAGE THE MECHANISM.

oh, NO--
THE RAY--
IT HAD NO EFFECT.!
APPARENTLY THIS IS NOT IDENTICAL TO THE PHENOMENON BARRY ENCOUNTERED.
PERHAPS THESE REACTIONS I INITIATED EARLIER WILL YIELD BETTER RESULTS THAN--
--HMMM. MOST UNFORTUNATE.
THESE BRAIN CELL CULTURES ARE SUPER-EVOLVING AT AN EXPONENTIAL RATE--
--WHILE THE TISSUE CULTURES ARE ATROPHYING! THE TRICKSTER'S RAY ALONE COULDN'T DO THIS! SOME-HOW THE MITOTIC PROPHASE HAS BEEN--
WALLY--!
--MY SKULL IS GOING TO EXPLODE!
YOU CAN EXPLAIN THE SCIENCE LATER! FOR NOW, JUST TELL ME WHAT IT MEANS!
IT MEANS MY BODY WILL GET WEAKER AS MY HEAD CONTINUES TO EXPAND. IN A FEW HOURS--

THERE MUST BE SOMETHING WE CAN--
RRRING!
OH, LET THE MACHINE ANSWER IT-- IT CAN'T BE AS IMPORTANT AS THIS!
LINDA! THIS IS JOHN AT THE STATION! IF YOU'RE THERE, PICK UP! IT'S AN EMERGENCY--!
"--SUPER-GORILLA GRODD IS ON A RAMPAGE!"
THAT'S RIGHT, PUNY ONES-- SCURRY AWAY LIKE THE MICE YOU ARE! YOU ARE NO MATCH FOR--
POLIC
1A12
--THE WRATH OF GRODD!
POLICE
I CARE NOTHING FOR YOUR BANKS OR YOUR POLICE! ALL I WANT IS--
--THE FLASH!

FACE ME, SPEEDSTER! I WILL LEVEL KEYSTONE CITY, IF THAT'S WHAT IT TAKES TO DRAW YOU OUT!
GRODD! THIS CANNOT BE A COINCIDENCE!
YOU'RE NOT GOING DOWN THERE, ARE YOU? NOT IN YOUR CONDITION?!

YOU HEARD HIS ULTIMATUM--
--IT'S ME--OR ALL OF KEYSTONE!
I MUST GO--
--BUT HERE IS WHAT I WANT YOU TO DO...

WHERE ARE YOU, WEST? EVEN THE MOST ENJOYABLE MINDLESS MAYHEM GROWS STALE EVENTUALLY!
KEEP FIRING! MAYBE FLASH JUST NEEDS A LITTLE NOISE TO WAKE HIM UP!
VOOOM!
KACHOOM!

HE'LL BE HERE SOON--I KNOW HIM! EVEN A DEVOLVED BRAIN WON'T KEEP HIM AWAY!
AND THEN--HE WILL BE MINE!

SIMPLY RUNNING HERE HAS EXHAUSTED ME--BUT I CAN'T ALLOW GRODD TO SUSPECT. MUST TRY TO SOUND CONFIDENT--NORMAL!
CEASE THIS IMPROPER BEHAVIOR, YOU GARGANTUAN MISCREANT!
FLASH!?
POL
HE'S BECOME SUPER-EVOLVED! MY RAY FAILED--BUT HOW? UNLESS--
--CIPHER!

MY STRENGTH IS DWINDLING--
--I MUST TRY TO DEFEAT HIM--
--RAPIDLY!
A PATHETIC DISPLAY, FLASH!
WHOOMP!
ALLOW ME TO END IT, BEFORE YOU EMBARRASS YOURSELF FURTHER!
DON'T LOSE CONSCIOUSNESS NOW, SPEEDSTER--
--THIS MOMENT WAS MEANT TO BE SHARED!
Oh, NO!
WALLY WAS SO SURE HE KNEW WHAT GRODD WOULD DO--BUT IF HE WAS WRONG--
--HE'S DEAD!
Oh, NO!
I'M NOT GOING TO LET THAT BLASTED APE STEAL MY MOMENT OF TRIUMPH!

I COULD KILL YOU NOW, FLASH--
--BUT HOW MUCH MORE SATISFYING IT WILL BE TO HAVE YOU AS MY SLAVE!
I KNEW--YOU WOULD COME TO THAT CONCLUSION--
A SINGLE BLAST FROM MY DEVOLUTION RAY--
--WILL ENABLE ME TO BEND YOU TO MY WILL! AND THIS TIME--
--THERE WILL BE NO INTERFERENCE FROM CIPHER!
WHO--?
OKAY, WALLY--IT LOOKS LIKE YOU WERE RIGHT ABOUT GRODD!
NOW LET'S HOPE YOU WERE RIGHT ABOUT THIS LITTLE GIZMO, TOO!
ANOTHER SHOT NOW, AT FULL POWER, WILL BLAST FLASH'S HEAD TO BITS!

ZZZZZK!
BRRAAK!
VREEEE!
AAAHH!
IT'S WORKING-- I'M RETURNING TO NORMAL!

I'M BACK, GRODD--
--AND I COULDN'T HAVE DONE IT WITHOUT YOU.!
WHAK!
WHAK!
POW!
THANKS!

REMIND ME TO ASK YOU ABOUT THIS CIPHER YOU MENTIONED--
--WHEN YOU WAKE UP!
MMM

WHEW! THAT WAS WAY TOO CLOSE!
YOU WEREN'T WORRIED, WERE YOU? I KNEW GRODD WOULD ZAP ME AGAIN--
--AND THE THINGIE I MADE WOULD COMBINE WITH HIS BEAM TO REVERSE THE EFFECTS!
BUT I ADMIT--I STILL DON'T GET HOW THE TRICKSTER'S OLD WEAPON ENTERS INTO IT!

OKAY, NOW YOU CAN EXPLAIN THE WEIRD SCIENCE BEHIND ALL THIS. IT'LL MAKE A GREAT STORY!
I HATE TO SPOIL YOUR SCOOP, HON--
--BUT NOW THAT I'M BACK TO NORMAL, I DON'T UNDERSTAND A BIT OF IT MYSELF!
WHAT?!

GRRRR...
HOW DO YOU WORK ONE OF THESE THINGS, ANYWAY...?
END

HA HA HA HA HA HA HA HA HA HA HA
DON'T MAKE US LAUGH!
The Joker's not the only one who can tell a good gag
Batman and Robin know a few rib-ticklers, too!
Why is a school football pitch always soggy?
Because the players are always dribbling!
Why is Europe like a frying pan?
Because it has Greece at the bottom!
What's the difference between 'unlawful' and 'illegal'?
Unlawful is against the law, illegal is a sick bird!
What's green and goes 'da-dit, da-dit, da-dit'?
Morse toad!
Robin, you missed cleaning your room yesterday, didn't you?
No, I didn't miss it one bit!
What bird always succeeds?
A budgie with no teeth!
How many ears does Captain Kirk have?
Three! A left ear, a right ear - and a final frontier!
How do you send a baby astronaut to sleep?
Rocket!
What's wet, black, floats on water and shouts 'knickers'?
Crude oil!
A HA HA HA HA HA HA HA HA HA

HAHAHAHAHAHAHAHAHAH
What's wet, black, floats on water and whispers 'undergarments'?
Refined oil!
How do you keep an idiot waiting?
I'll tell you tomorrow!
What's black, white and red all over?
A penguin with sunburn?
Why are there no aspirins in the jungle?
Because the parrots eat 'em all!
Why don't most cats shave?
Because eight out of ten prefer whiskers!
What do you get if you cross grass seed with a cow?
A lawn mooer!
I've just met a government artist, Robin!
Don't tell me, he 'draws the dole'!
Why can't a bicycle stand up?
Because it's two-tired!
Our dog is just like one of the family!
Really! Which one?
HAHAHAHAHAHAHAHAHAHA

RACE AGAINST TIME!

Batman and Robin to the rescue! In one minute, The Penguin is going to wreak havoc on Gotham City! Only one of these paths will take the duo into the city in under sixty seconds, but which one? Take a guess, then see if you're right!

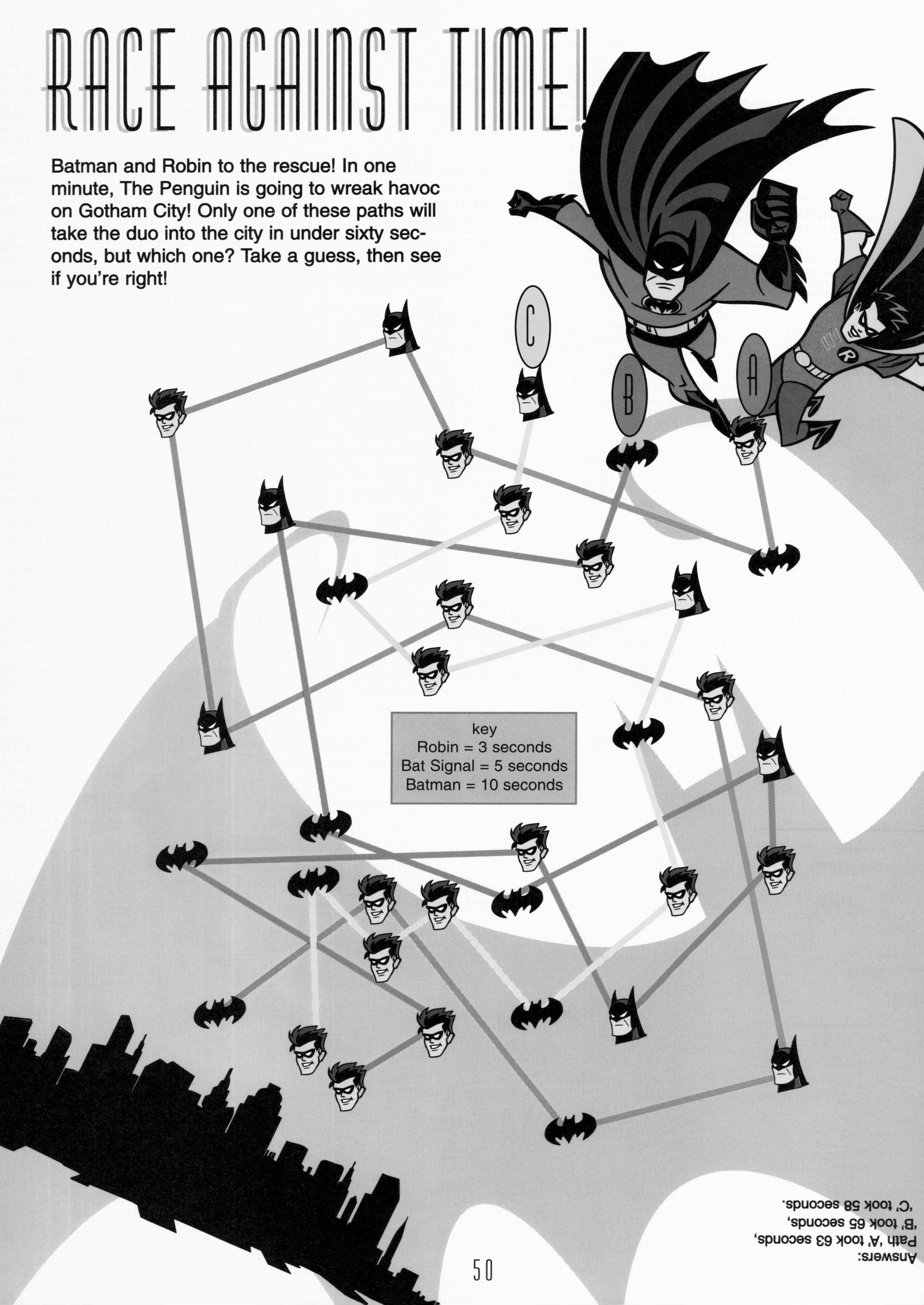

Answers:
Path 'A' took 63 seconds,
'B' took 65 seconds,
'C' took 58 seconds.

AFTER THE MURDER OF HIS PARENTS, YOUNG BRUCE WAYNE DEDICATED HIS LIFE TO AVENGING THEIR DEATHS. NOW HE WAGES WAR AGAINST GOTHAM CITY'S CRIMINALS AS BATMAN, THE DARK KNIGHT! FEW OF HIS FOES ARE AS BEAUTIFUL OR AS INSANE AS THE DEADLY MISTRESS OF PLANTS AND TOXINS -- POISON IVY!

BATMAN® IN CRUISE TO NIGHTMARE

ANOTHER NIGHT, ANOTHER COSTUME PARTY.
ON GOES THE MASK, THE SUIT, AND ALL THE ACCESSORIES NEEDED TO MAKE THE ILLUSION COMPLETE.

THAT'S ME. THE ONE WEARING THE TUXEDO AND THE FORCED SMILE.
BRUCE WAYNE: BILLIONAIRE, SOCIALITE, PLAYBOY.
0TH ANNUAL WAYNE FOUNDATION CHARITY DRIVE

RRRROO ARR!
LOOKS LIKE I'LL BE NEEDING THE OTHER COSTUME.
BRAKKAA BBRAKKA BRRAKKA BRAK
EEEEEEK!

PAUL DINI WRITER · BRUCE TIMM ARTIST · MARK CHIARELLO COLORIST · STARKINGS/COMICRAFT LETTERING · CHARLES KOCHMAN EDITOR

A SEA SERPENT MADE OF SEAWEED...
IT'S A GIMMICK AS BRILLIANT AND DEADLY AS THE WOMAN WHO CREATED IT...

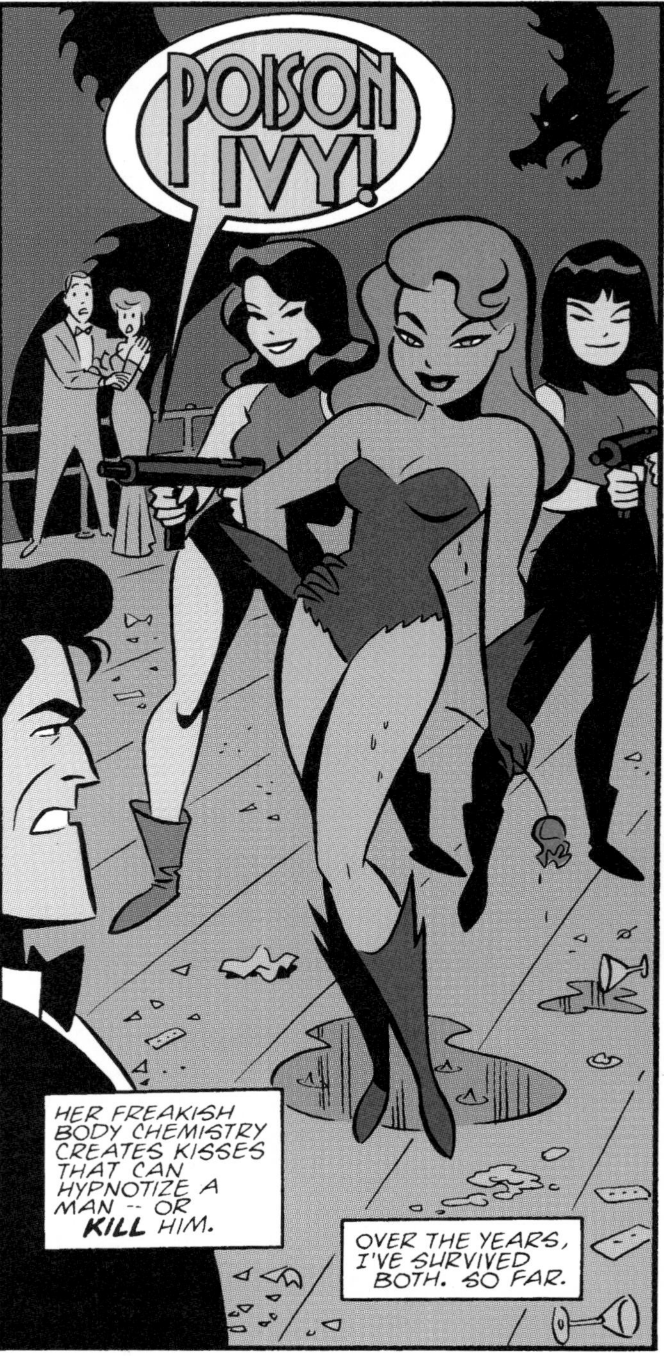

POISON IVY!
HER FREAKISH BODY CHEMISTRY CREATES KISSES THAT CAN HYPNOTIZE A MAN -- OR KILL HIM.
OVER THE YEARS, I'VE SURVIVED BOTH. SO FAR.

YOU LOOK LIKE YOU'RE NOT HAPPY TO SEE ME, BRUCE.

I THOUGHT AFTER ALL OUR PREVIOUS ENCOUNTERS, YOU'D HAVE SOME FEELING FOR ME.
I DO.
IT'S CALLED "DISGUST."
YOU KNOW THIS WOMAN, BRUCE?

UNFORTUNATELY. HER REAL NAME IS PAMELA ISLEY, THOUGH SHE LIKES TO CALL HERSELF POISON IVY. AS YOU CAN SEE FROM HER "PET," SHE'S GOT A WAY WITH PLANTS.

AND WITH MEN, TOO, Hmmm?
YOU DIDN'T COME HERE TO PICK UP A DATE.
0TH ANNUAL
YNE FOUNDATION
ARITY DRIV
PLEASE GIVE

NOT ORIGINALLY, BUT NOW THAT YOU'RE HERE, I'M TEMPTED TO ADD YOU TO MY HAUL.

YOU'RE NOT TAKING THE CHARITY MONEY!
Oh NO?
SNAP!
WAYNE FOUND
CHARITY
PLEASE GIVE

IT'S NOT THE EASIEST WAY TO MAKE AN EXIT...
OOOOOOOOF!
WHAM!
NO!

SPLASH!
POOR BRUCE. VERY CUTE...
...BUT VERY STUPID!
...BUT IT WILL HAVE TO DO.

BANG!

YOU HEARTLESS WITCH! YOU JUST MURDERED A MAN IN COLD BLOOD!
WHAT'S YOUR POINT?

THE LONGER IVY'S PET IS OUT OF THE WATER, THE DRIER IT GETS.
I'M SURE THE CAPTAIN WON'T MIND MY BORROWING HIS FLARE GUN...

ARROOOO
FWOOM!
POP!
HEY!
WHAT GIVES?

LOOK OUT!

THUD!
OOF
BAM!
UGHH

IVY..?

I'M A LOVER, NOT A FIGHTER, DARLING.
BEHIND ME--
!
--TOO LATE.
SHE KISSES ME AND THE TOXINS IN HER BLOODSTREAM SET MY BRAIN ON FIRE.

STRUGGLE ALL YOU WANT, HANDSOME.
IT JUST MAKES IT ALL THE MORE PAINFUL FOR YOU AND ALL THE MORE ENJOYABLE FOR ME.
UHHHHH..

CAN'T FOCUS...
...HAVE TO...
...END THIS...

...ANY WAY I CAN!
PAFF!

BONK!

OOOhhhh

LATER...
THANK HEAVEN THE COAST GUARD WAS THERE TO FISH YOU OUT.
FROM NOW ON, YOU'D BETTER LEAVE THE ACTS OF FOOLHARDY BRAVERY TO SOMEONE LIKE BATMAN.

BELIEVE ME -- I WILL.
THE END

CLOCKS

Superman's late for his date with Lois Lane! Take Superman to the clock tower by moving in any direction. With each move, you must make sure there is never more than an hour's difference between clock faces!

SHARE AND SHARE ALIKE!

Connecting the lettered and numbered points, divide this picture into six sections, each containing one Batman, one Robin and one batsignal. There's just one catch! You can only draw three straight lines!

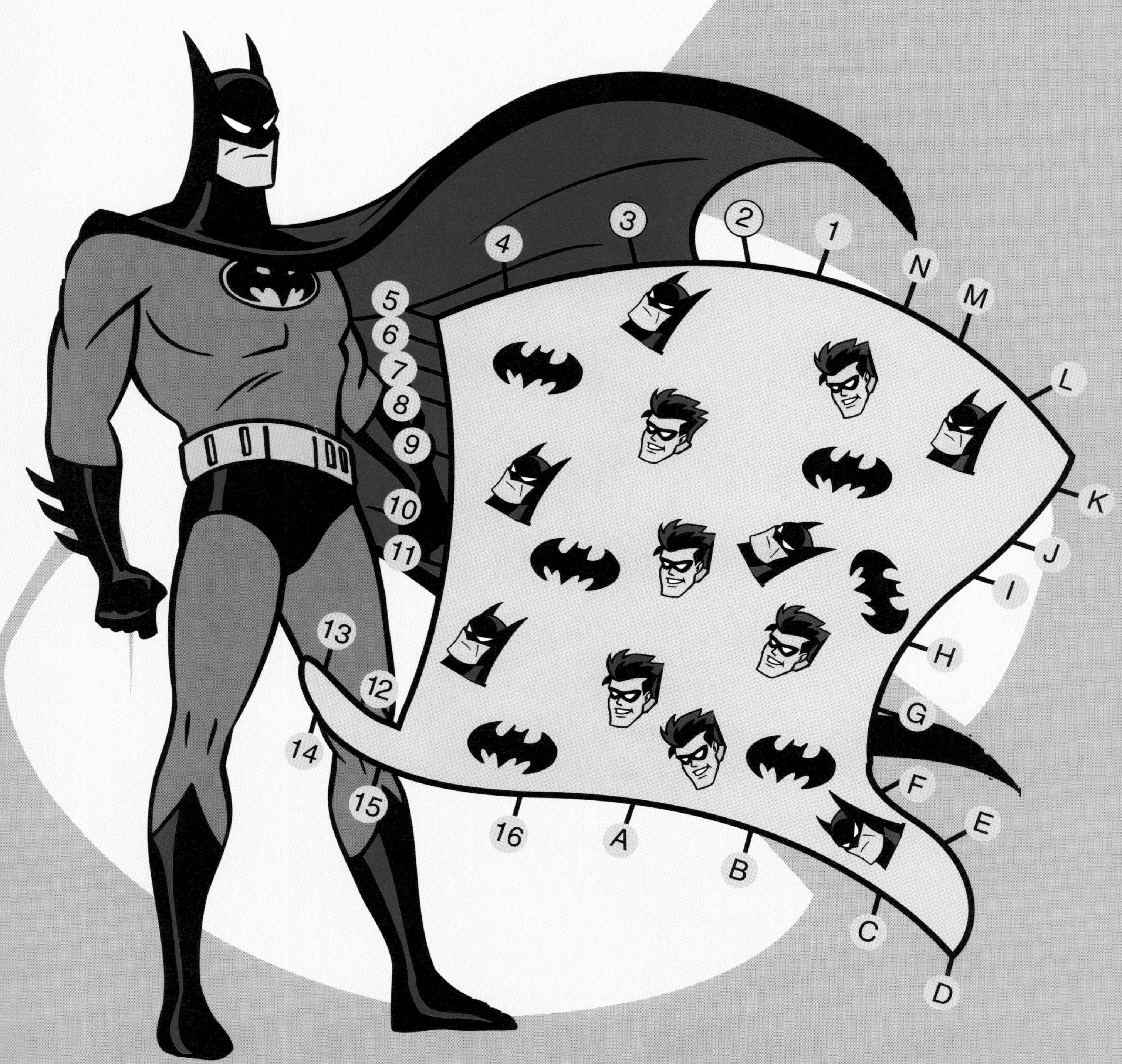

Answer:
Draw lines meeting at the following points: 1-A, 8-I, 11-G.

GRRROOWWLL

FASTER!
HUFF
THAK
THAK
THAK

GOT TO GO FASTER!
HUFF
HUFF
THAK THAK

IF SHE CATCHES ME, I'M--
PANT
PANT
THAK THAK

DEAD EN
oh, no...

I'LL HIDE! COVER MYSELF UP SO SHE CAN'T--

--FIND ME...

NO! IT'S NOT HER--

"--IT'S THAT SUPERHERO--
THE ONE CALLED...
WONDER WOMAN
CREATED BY WILLIAM MOULTON MARSTON
I'M ALWAYS HAPPY TO HELP THE COAST GUARD, BUT RESCUING THOSE BOATERS HAS MADE ME LATE!
I HOPE I HAVEN'T KEPT HELENA WAITING TOO LONG.
SHE WAS SO ANXIOUS TO BEGIN CATALOGUING THE NEW ACQUISITIONS THAT ARE ARRIVING AT THE MUSEUM TONIGHT!
Channel 27 YOUR MEGASTATION call your cable company!
YOU CAN'T CHEETAH AN HONEST MAN!
STEVE VANCE-SCRIPT+BREAKDOWNS JOHN DELANEY-PENCILS RON BOYD-INKS BOB LeROSE-COLORS TIM HARKINS-LETTERS FRANK BERRIOS-ASSISTS KC CARLSON-EDITOR
PUURRRR

POLICE--AT THE MUSEUM! BUT WHY?
MUSEUM OF ANTIQUITIES

HELENA! WHAT IS--
GREAT HERA!

DIANA! AM I GLAD TO SEE YOU!
MIKE! WHAT HAS HAPPENED? WHERE IS HELENA?

SHE'S GONE, DIANA. SHE'S BEEN KIDNAPPED -- OR WORSE!
AND FROM THE LOOK OF THINGS THE PARTY RESPONSIBLE IS--
CHEETAH!

THESE SCRATCHES ARE INDEED HER CLAW MARKS!
IN HER HUMAN FORM SHE IS ARCHAEOLOGIST BARBARA MINERVA. I MUST ASSUME SHE WAS AFTER SOME-THING IN THIS CRATE.

IF WE CAN FIND THE MANIFEST LISTING THE SHIPMENT'S CONTENTS, PERHAPS WE CAN DETERMINE WHAT--
I CAN TELL YOU--

--SHE WAS AFTER THIS!
YOU MUST PROTECT ME, WONDER WOMAN! I BEG YOU--DON'T LET HER GET ME!
WHO ARE YOU?! WHAT DO YOU KNOW ABOUT ALL THIS?! WHERE'S HELENA SANDSMARK?!
I-I--
ALLOW ME, MIKE. MY GOLDEN LASSO WILL ELICIT THE TRUTH.
PLEASE SIT DOWN, MR.--?
MY NAME IS JACOB WALTERS. I'M IN THE, ER, IMPORT BUSINESS.
...WITH JUST THE OCCASIONAL BIT OF SMUGGLING ON THE SIDE.
I HELPED TO EXPEDITE THE SHIPMENT OF THESE ARTIFACTS FROM THEIR NATIVE LAND.
I RECEIVED A CALL FROM DR. MINERVA. SHE OFFERED ME A HANDSOME SUM SIMPLY FOR INFORMING HER OF THE SHIPMENT'S ARRIVAL.
I AGREED. I SAW NO HARM IN IT. I-I...
...I DIDN'T KNOW. I SWEAR. I DIDN'T KNOW.
"I DELIVERED THE CRATE THIS EVENING. WE HAD JUST OPENED IT WHEN... THAT CREATURE BURST IN."
"DR. SANDSMARK TRIED TO RESIST. IT WAS HOPELESS! BUT WHILE CHEETAH WAS DISTRACTED, I GRABBED THE PACKAGE--"
"--AND RAN AWAY."
"I SUPPOSE I THOUGHT I COULD USE THE ARTIFACT TO BUY MY SAFETY--BUT THEN I REALIZED THAT SHE WAS CERTAIN TO TRACK ME DOWN AND--"
"I-I DON'T THINK SHE'S THE NEGOTIATING TYPE."
I SAW YOU ARRIVE, SO I CAME BACK. YOU'LL PROTECT ME, WON'T YOU?
YOU RAT! YOU SET UP DR. SANDSMARK, AND LEFT HER TO--
WAIT, MIKE.
WHAT IS IN THE PACKAGE, MR. WALTERS?

DON'T TELL ME YOU GOT A STATUE OF A BLACK BIRD IN THERE...
INDEED NOT, OFFICER-- THOUGH YOU MIGHT CALL IT THE STUFF NIGHTMARES ARE MADE OF.

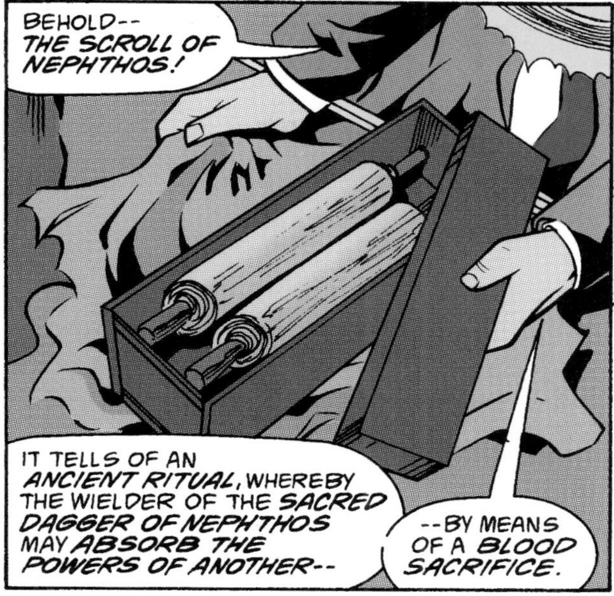
BEHOLD-- THE SCROLL OF NEPHTHOS!
IT TELLS OF AN ANCIENT RITUAL, WHEREBY THE WIELDER OF THE SACRED DAGGER OF NEPHTHOS MAY ABSORB THE POWERS OF ANOTHER--
--BY MEANS OF A BLOOD SACRIFICE.

"SACRED DAGGER"? YOU MEAN--
WAS THIS BLADE ALSO IN THE CRATE?
Y-YES.

CHEETAH'S PLOT IS CLEAR NOW. SHE HAS THE DAGGER...
...AND SHE HAS YOU PEGGED TO BE HER "BLOOD SACRIFICE!"

I AM CERTAIN SHE ALLOWED WALTERS TO ESCAPE, SO THAT THE SCROLL WOULD FALL INTO MY HANDS.
HEY, SCHORR--CALL FOR YOU ON THE CAR RADIO!
'SCUSE ME, DIANA.

I COPY THAT, THANKS-- SCHORR OUT.
WHAT NEWS?
Gift Shop
CHEETAH WAS SPOTTED CROSSING THE GATEWAY BRIDGE-- SHE'S LEAVING TOWN!

THEN I MUST FOLLOW!
HEY! YOU'RE NOT TAKING THE SCROLL, ARE YOU? WE'VE GOTTA KEEP IT AWAY FROM CHEETAH!

NO, MIKE--I MUST TAKE IT TO HER IN ORDER TO FREE HELENA. IT IS MY FAULT THAT SHE WAS CAPTURED. IF I HAD NOT BEEN LATE--
--YOU MIGHT BOTH BE DEAD NOW!

C'MON, DIANA--IT'S A TRAP! DON'T BE A SUCKER!
I WILL TAKE EVERY PRECAUTION, MIKE.

CHEETAH WOULD NEVER HAVE BEEN SEEN BY THE POLICE--UNLESS SHE WANTED TO BE! CLEARLY, SHE WISHES ME TO FOLLOW--
--AND I BELIEVE I KNOW WHERE!

STRANGE... ALTHOUGH WE HAVE BEEN BITTER FOES, I FEEL A CERTAIN CONNECTION WITH BARBARA.
HER POWERS DERIVE FROM THE ANCIENT GODS... FROM THE EARTH ITSELF...

"... AND I, TOO, AM OF THE EARTH. MY MOTHER, HIPPOLYTA, QUEEN OF THE AMAZONS, FORMED ME FROM THE CLAY OF THE ISLE OF THEMYSCIRA.

"MY POWERS, MY VERY LIFE, WERE GRANTED TO ME BY THE GODS."

"ON THAT MYSTIC ISLAND, HIDDEN FROM MORTAL VIEW, I WAS RAISED AS A PRINCESS."

"BUT EVENTUALLY I RELINQUISHED MY IMMORTALITY AND CAME HERE, TO THE WORLD OF MEN, AS AN EMISSARY OF MY PEOPLE."

"I KNOW WHAT IT IS TO BE OF TWO WORLDS... YET NOT FULLY AT HOME IN EITHER."

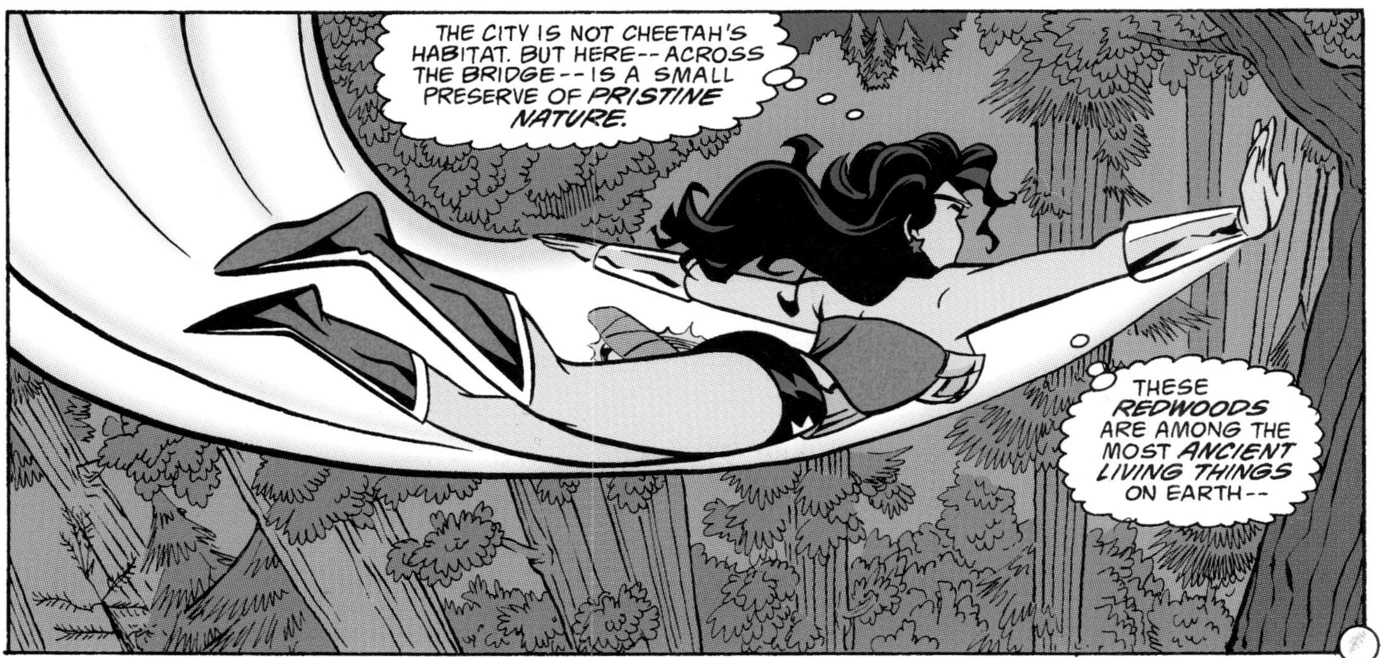

THE CITY IS NOT CHEETAH'S HABITAT. BUT HERE--ACROSS THE BRIDGE--IS A SMALL PRESERVE OF PRISTINE NATURE.
THESE REDWOODS ARE AMONG THE MOST ANCIENT LIVING THINGS ON EARTH--

"--SURELY THIS IS WHERE I WILL FIND HER."
FIRE BURN BRIGHT--BRIGHT AS THE GLITTERING EYE OF NEPHTHOS!
OOHHH...
SO--DE SLEEPER WAKES!
WH-WHO ARE YOU? WHAT AM I DOING H--
THAT DAGGER--THE BLADE OF NEPHTHOS! YOU'RE PREPARING A SACRIFICE!
CORRECT, DOCTOR. BUT DE CEREMONY CANNOT BEGIN UNTIL WE HAVE DE SACRED SCROLL AS WELL!
THESE ARE PRICELESS CULTURAL ARTIFACTS! YOU CAN'T --
INDEED I CAN. BUT DO NOT FEAR-- YOU ARE NOT DE INTENDED VICTIM. NOR WILL I WIELD DE BLADE.
DAT IS FOR MY MISTRESS, BARBARA MINERVA. THROUGH DIS CEREMONY, SHE WILL ABSORB DE LIFE FORCE OF SOMEONE FAR MORE POWERFUL DAN YOU--
I BELIEVE YOU ARE REFERRING TO ME.

I COME HOPING FOR PEACE, CHUMA. MUST THERE BE CONFLICT BETWEEN US?
I RESPECT YOU, WONDER WOMAN--BUT I SERVE DE WILL OF BARBARA MINERVA!

AND WHERE IS YOUR MISTRESS? I THOUGHT I WOULD FIND HER HERE.

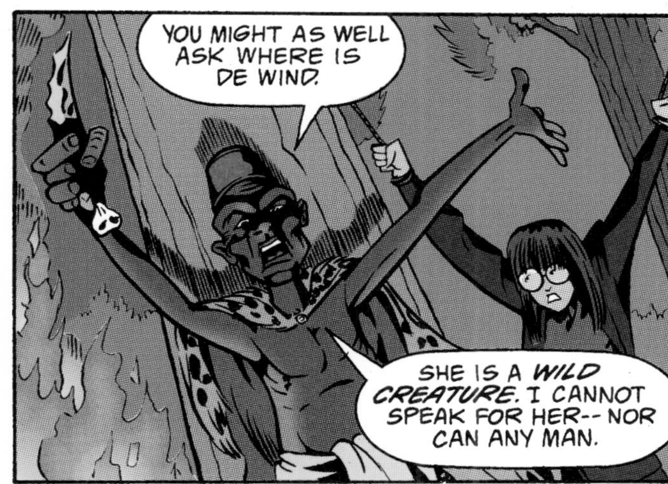
YOU MIGHT AS WELL ASK WHERE IS DE WIND.
SHE IS A WILD CREATURE. I CANNOT SPEAK FOR HER--NOR CAN ANY MAN.

I SEE YOU HAVE BROUGHT DE SCROLL OF NEPHTHOS!
DIANA--NO!
CHEETAH INTENDS TO KILL YOU--TO STEAL YOUR POWERS!
YOU MUSTN'T GIVE UP THE SCROLL--IT WILL COST YOU YOUR LIFE!
I WILL GLADLY TRADE THE SCROLL FOR YOUR FREEDOM, HELENA--
--AS FOR MY LIFE, CHEETAH WILL HAVE TO CLAIM IT BY FORCE!

I BELIEVE DOSE TERMS ARE ACCEPTABLE.

GRRRRR...

CHEETAH!

HER CLAWS ARE LETHAL! I HOPE MY BRACELETS WILL SHIELD ME --
CHANG!

--UNTIL I CAN SUBDUE HER!

OOF!

WHOKK!

SHE MOVES WITH THE QUICKNESS OF HERMES HIMSELF!
I MUST DRAW HER AWAY FROM HELENA!

I NOW SEE ANOTHER REASON CHEETAH CHOSE THIS SITE.

THESE GREAT TREES ARE AN OBSTACLE FOR ME...

...AND AN ALLY FOR HER.

IN THIS ENVIRONMENT, WE ARE EVENLY MATCHED! BUT I--

I'VE LOST HER-- OR HAS SHE LOST ME?
WHAAK!
Ahh!
THOOOM!
RRROOWWLLL!

THONK!

SHE IS PREPARING TO SPRING! I MUST BE READY FOR HER TO--

NO! SHE IS RETURNING TO HELENA!

MAY ATHENA CURSE ME FOR A FOOL! I SHOULD HAVE EXPECTED SUCH A TACTIC!

oh! SHE'S BACK! DOES THIS MEAN THAT DIANA IS--

STAY YOUR HAND, BARBARA MINERVA--

--OR I WILL DESTROY THE SCROLL!
NO, AMAZON--YOU MUST RELINQUISH DE SCROLL, OR YOUR FRIEND WILL PERISH!

I WILL DO WHAT I MUST. THE DECISION IS CHEETAH'S--
--OR, PERHAPS, BETWEEN CHEETAH AND BARBARA MINERVA!

DON'T DO IT, DIANA! THAT SCROLL IS AN IRREPLACEABLE TREASURE!

RRRRRR

AS ARE YOU, HELENA!

ROOOWWRRR!
NO!

FWOOSH!

SNIK

HSSSSS!

oh, MY...
YOU MAY BE MORE COMFORTABLE IF YOU DON'T LOOK DOWN.

OOOWWAR RRRR

THANK YOU SO MUCH FOR RESCUING ME, DIANA -- BUT THE SCROLLS -- THEIR LOSS --
-- DID NOT HAPPEN. THEY ARE QUITE SAFE.
WHAT?!
GIFT S OP

BEFORE I LEFT, I SUBSTITUTED A REPRODUCTION OF A SUMERIAN SCROLL FROM OUR GIFT SHOP.
IT WAS A GAMBLE, BUT...
IT PAID OFF! THANK GOODNESS! I CAN HARDLY WAIT TO EXAMINE THE REAL THING...
Come on in OPEN
AUTHENTIC REPRODUCTION SUMERIAN SCROLLS $24.95

"... AFTER I SLEEP FOR A WEEK!"
STUDYING THIS SCROLL HAS BEEN AN EDUCATION, DIANA! IT'S AN AMAZING FIND!
BUT IT'S FRUSTRATING KNOWING THAT I CAN NEVER PUBLISH MY RESEARCH!
STORAGE AUTHORIZED PERSONNEL ONLY

NOR CAN THE SCROLL BE PUT ON PUBLIC DISPLAY. WE CANNOT RISK CHEETAH LEARNING THAT IT WAS NOT DESTROYED.
WELL, EVEN IF SHE DOES COME LOOKING FOR IT, I THINK IT'S SAFE--

-- NOT EVEN A SUPERVILLAIN COULD FIGURE OUT THIS MUSEUM'S FILING SYSTEM!
END

PLANET CONFUSION

Can Superman save our planet? A huge meteorite is spinning out of control - and heading towards Earth! Re-arrange the letters on the meteorite to spell the name of eight planets.

Answer:
The planets are: PLUTO, MARS, JUPITER, URANUS, SATURN, MERCURY, VENUS, NEPTUNE.

BOXED-IN!

Before Batman can catch The Penguin, he has to work-out how to trace this design without lifting his finger off the page - and without passing over the same line twice! Can you help him?

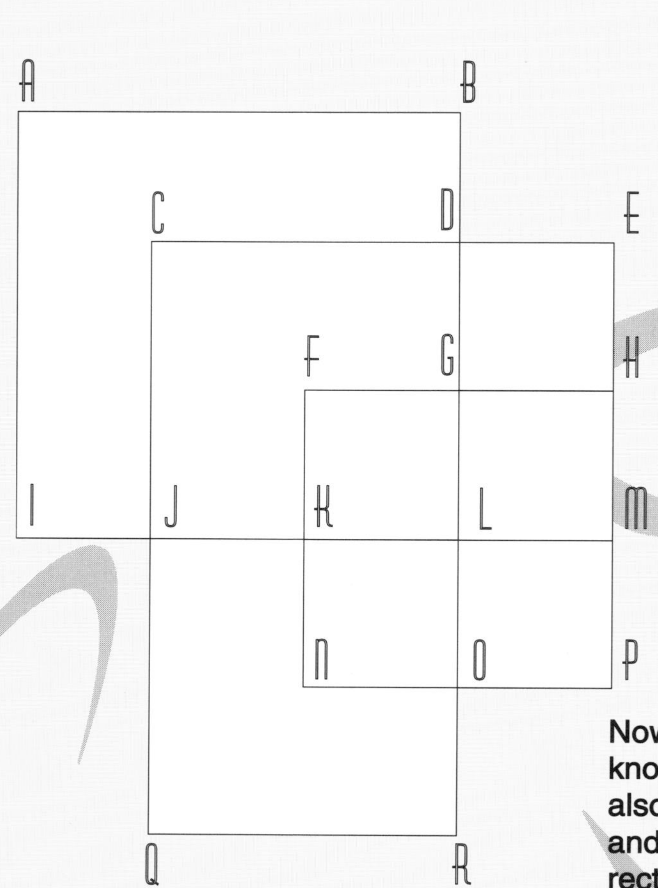

Now Robin has a puzzle to ponder over! He knows The Penguin appears in rectangle 'B'. He also appears in the rectangle formed by taking 'B' and 'C' together. But who appears in the most rectangles - The Penguin or Poison Ivy?

A B C
D E F G
H I

Answer: (1) H/F/N/P/E/C/Q/R/B/A/I/M. (2) The Penguin appears in 10 rectangles: AB, ABC, ABCGFED, ABCGFEDHI, ABGF, ABGFH, B, BC, BCFED, BF. Poison Ivy appears in 13 rectangles: ABCGFED, ABCGFEDHI, BCFED, CED, CEDI, E, ED, EDI, FE, FED, GFE, GFED, GFEDHI.

ISN'T IT DRY YET? GEEZ LOUISE--THE PACKAGE SAID TEN MINUTES!
MMMPH!
MUST BE THE HUMIDITY. THIS WEATHER MAKES ME SWEAT LIKE A PIG--I DON'T UNDERSTAND WHY THE BOSS LIVES ON THIS CRUMMY ISLAND.

NO TAXES, BASIL! I WOULDN'T MIND A LITTLE SWEAT IF IT SAVED ME $50 MILL A YEAR!
PLUS, BOCA GORDO'S GOT NO EXTRADITION TREATY WITH THE U.S.!
BEST FISHES MR D
CHADWICK'S CONCRETE MIX

I SEE WHAT YOU MEAN. AN' OF COURSE MR.D LOVES THE FISHING HERE, ESPECIALLY THE BIG STUFF-- SAILFISH, MARLIN--

--SHARKS.
MMMHHKK!
NOW, NOW, FRED--DON'T COMPLAIN. YOU BROUGHT THIS ON YOURSELF.

YOU STOLE A BIG SHIPMENT OF EXPERIMENTAL RUSSIAN WEAPONS, SOLD IT TO A RIVAL OUTFIT, THEN TRIED TO JUGGLE MR. D'S BOOKS TO COVER YOUR TRACKS!
WORD IS THOSE ARMS ARE GONNA HELP SOME OF MR. D'S ENEMIES BREAK JAIL, SO YOU CAN'T BLAME HIM FOR BEING UPSET!
MMM-NN! MMM-NN!
OKAY, OMAR--THE CEMENT'S READY--

--LET'S DO FREDDIE!
MMMMMNNNN!
SPLAAASH!

UNUSUAL SWIMMING ATTIRE--EVEN FOR A SURFACE-DWELLER!
MMMLUB!
HMM...
STEVE "SHARKY" VANCE SCRIPT
JOHN "DOLPHIN" DELANEY PENCILS
RON "MANTA RAY" BOYD INKS
TIM "HAMMERHEAD" HARKINS LETTERS
BOB "BARNACLE" LE ROSE COLORS
FRANK "BIG FISH" BERRIOS ASSISTANT EDITS
KC "MRS. PAUL" CARLSON EDITS
BEST FISHES MR. D.
AQUAMAN
FAMILY MATTERS

ah, BASIL--IF ONLY ALL OF LIFE'S PROBLEMS WERE AS EASILY SOLVED.
I HEAR YA, MAN. LIKE, I'VE GOT THIS RASH ON MY--
GURGLE GURGLE

PTHOOEY!

WHAT KIND OF--?
IT'S COMING RIGHT--

OWWW!
KRRRUNCH!

ahk-ahk -ahk-
-AQUAMAN!
WHEN WILL YOU PEOPLE REALIZE THAT THE OCEANS ARE NOT YOUR GARBAGE CAN!
I'M IN A HURRY AT THE MOMENT, SO I'M ONLY GOING TO SAY THIS ONCE--

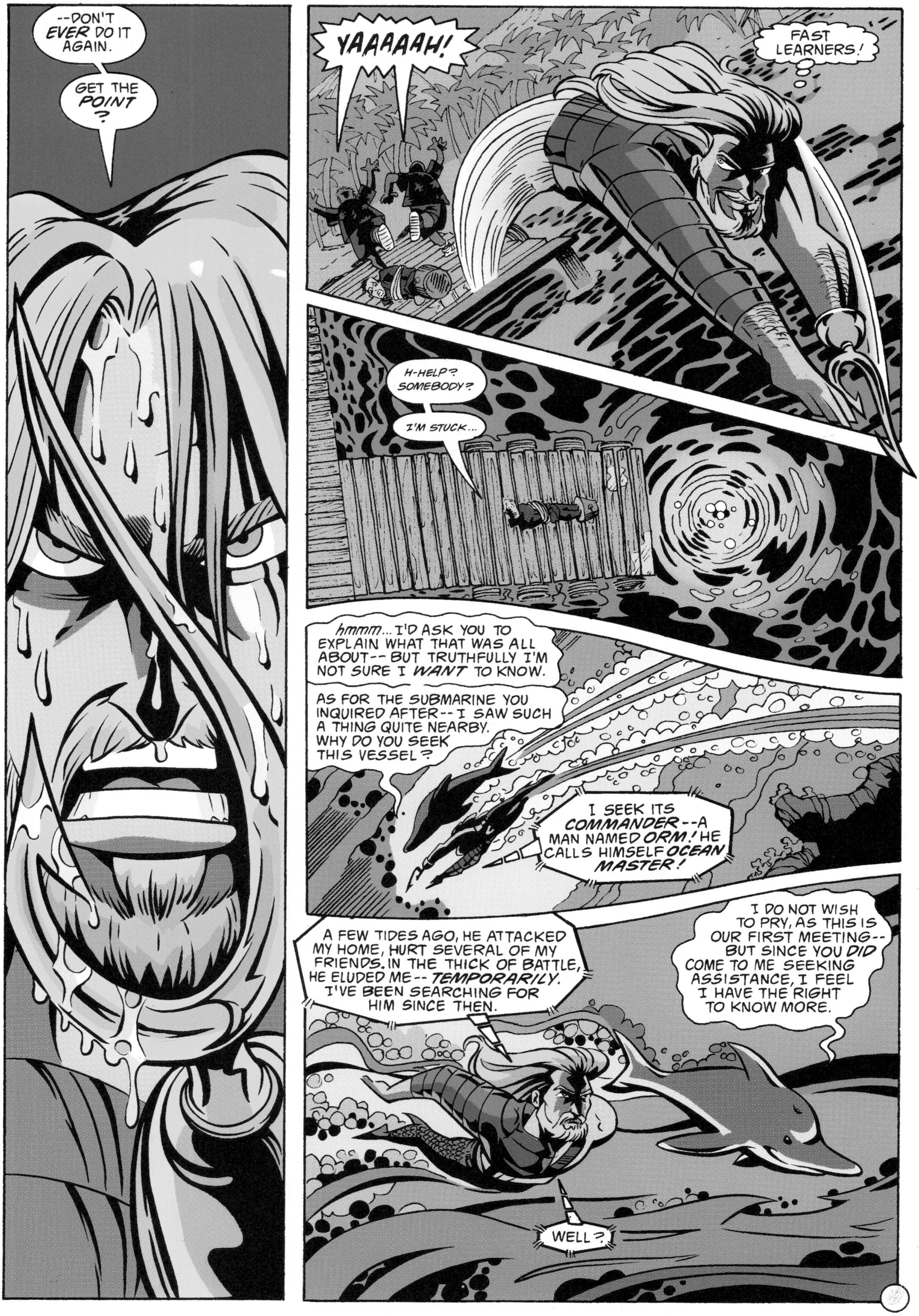

YAAAAAH!

FAST LEARNERS!

H-HELP? SOMEBODY?

I'M STUCK...

hmmm... I'D ASK YOU TO EXPLAIN WHAT THAT WAS ALL ABOUT-- BUT TRUTHFULLY I'M NOT SURE I WANT TO KNOW.

AS FOR THE SUBMARINE YOU INQUIRED AFTER-- I SAW SUCH A THING QUITE NEARBY. WHY DO YOU SEEK THIS VESSEL?

I SEEK ITS COMMANDER--A MAN NAMED ORM! HE CALLS HIMSELF OCEAN MASTER!

A FEW TIDES AGO, HE ATTACKED MY HOME, HURT SEVERAL OF MY FRIENDS. IN THE THICK OF BATTLE, HE ELUDED ME-- TEMPORARILY. I'VE BEEN SEARCHING FOR HIM SINCE THEN.

I DO NOT WISH TO PRY, AS THIS IS OUR FIRST MEETING-- BUT SINCE YOU DID COME TO ME SEEKING ASSISTANCE, I FEEL I HAVE THE RIGHT TO KNOW MORE.

WELL?

I HAVE HEARD MY BRETHREN SPEAK OF YOU WITH RESPECT-- THEY CALLED YOU "SWIMMER."
THAT NAME WAS GIVEN TO ME BY MY DOLPHIN MOTHER.
DOLPHIN MOTHER? IF THAT WERE TRUE, THEN WE, TOO, WOULD BE BRETHREN. BUT-- NO OFFENSE -- YOU ARE TOO UGLY TO HAVE BEEN BORN A DOLPHIN.
AND OCEAN MASTER? I KNOW YOU HAVE MANY ENEMIES -- WHY YOUR SINGLE-MINDED PURSUIT OF THIS ONE?
YOU HAVE AN UNUSUAL FAMILY, SWIMMER.
YOU COULD SAY THAT.
HE IS AN EVIL MAN--
--AND HE IS MY BROTHER.
"MY FATHER IS A RATHER MYSTERIOUS WIZARD NAMED ATLAN. MY MOTHER WAS ATLANNA, QUEEN OF ATLANTIS.
"WHEN I WAS BORN, MY FAIR HAIR WAS THOUGHT TO BE THE MARK OF AN ANCIENT CURSE, SO I WAS LEFT TO SUFFOCATE ON AN EXPOSED REEF.
"BUT UNLIKE OTHER ATLANTEANS, I CAN BREATHE AIR AS WELL AS WATER, SO I SURVIVED.
"A DOLPHIN NAMED PORM FOUND ME, RAISED ME-- MOTHERED ME.
"NOT UNTIL I REACHED ADULTHOOD DID I DISCOVER MY TRUE ATLANTEAN HERITAGE.
"OCEAN MASTER IS ALSO ATLAN'S SON, BY AN INUIT WOMAN. HE FEELS THAT EVERYTHING OF MINE -- MY POWERS, MY PRIMACY BENEATH THE WAVES -- IS RIGHTFULLY HIS!

"WE SEEM FATED TO CLASH. LEGENDS SAY THAT, FROM GENERATION TO GENERATION, BROTHERS WILL ALWAYS BATTLE FOR THE THRONE OF ATLANTIS."
THE THRONE OF ATLANTIS-- ONCE AGAIN, IT WAS WITHIN MY GRASP--
--AND ONCE AGAIN, I WAS FOILED BY MY ACCURSED BROTHER! NOT ONLY DID HE THWART MY PLANS--
--HE VERY NEARLY SANK THIS VERY EXPENSIVE SUBMARINE!
TO MAKE MATTERS WORSE, WHEN I SURFACED TO MAKE EMERGENCY REPAIRS, MY CREW JUMPED SHIP--
--FORCING ME TO REPLACE THEM WITH WHATEVER HALF-WITTED LOWLIFES WERE AVAILABLE AT THE NEAREST PORT!
NOW I HAVE TO ATTEMPT MAKESHIFT REPAIRS IN TRANSIT, UNTIL I CAN REACH A SAFE HARBOR.
THESE HUMILIATIONS ARE ALL AQUAMAN'S FAULT! I MAY BE LICKING MY WOUNDS NOW-- BUT WHEN THEY ARE HEALED, I'LL MAKE HIM PAY FOR--
SIR? THE BULKHEAD IN THE TORPEDO ROOM IS LEAKING AGAIN. YOUR ORDERS?
MAYBE YOU COULD STAND AROUND AND WATCH THE WATER LEVEL RISE UNTIL YOU DROWN!
FIX IT, YOU IDIOT-- FIX IT!
CALM YOURSELF, ORM! REMEMBER--IT'S THE LEADER WHO MATTERS-- THESE MEN ARE BUT RAW CLAY, TO BE MOLDED BY MY WILL!
THEY MAY NOT LOOK LIKE MUCH NOW, BUT WITH MY STRATEGIC BRILLIANCE, I'LL HAVE THIS LOT READY TO CRUSH AQUAMAN IN A FEW DAYS!
IN FACT, I ALREADY HAVE THE BEGINNINGS OF A NEW PLAN-
HAND ME THAT THINGIE--
HEY! WATCH IT!
KA-LUNK!
uh-oh...
SPLAASH!
SIGH... WELL, MAYBE IN A FEW WEEKS...
AT LEAST I HAVE THE LUXURY OF TIME! AFTER ALL...

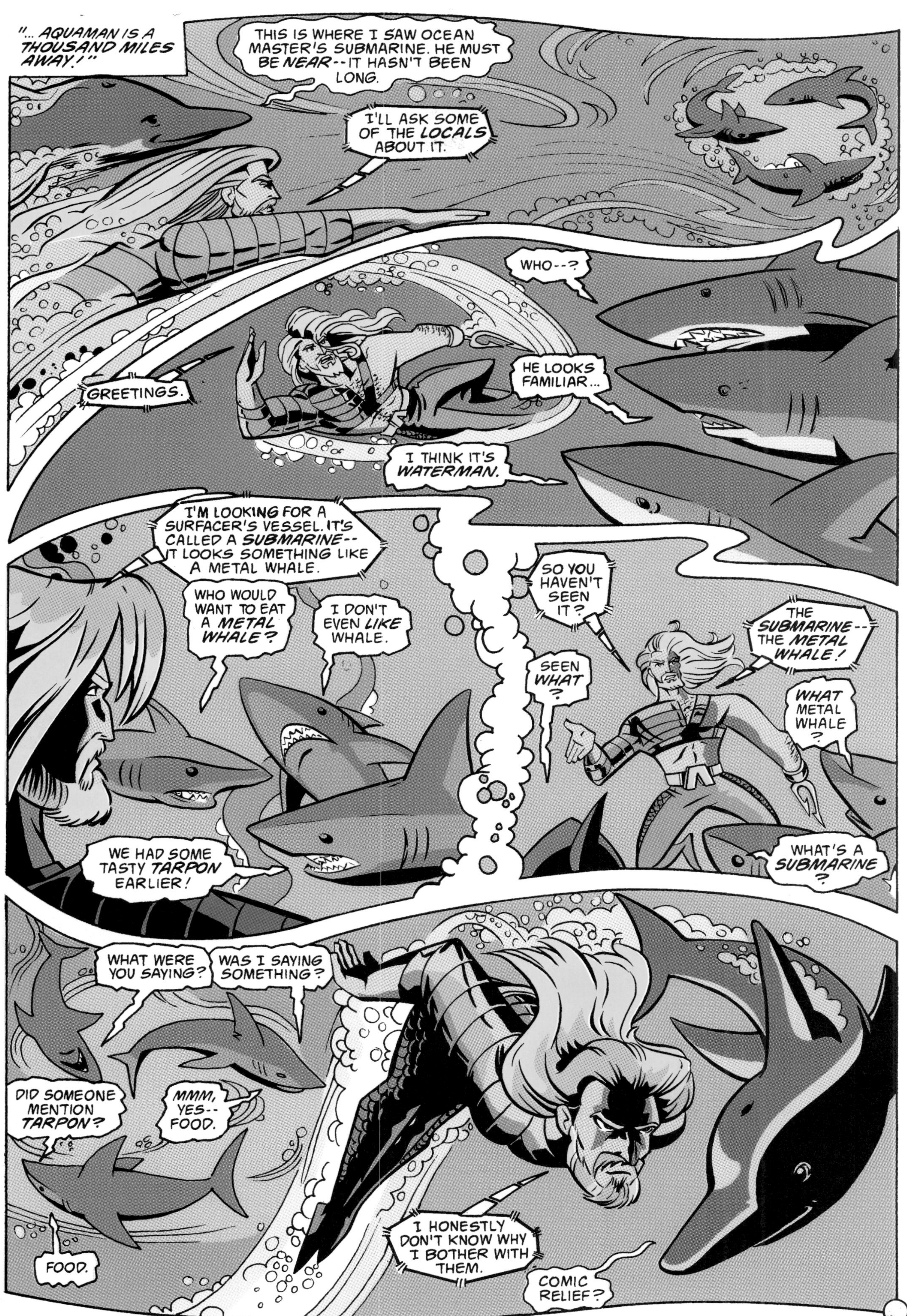
"... AQUAMAN IS A THOUSAND MILES AWAY!"
THIS IS WHERE I SAW OCEAN MASTER'S SUBMARINE. HE MUST BE NEAR--IT HASN'T BEEN LONG.
I'LL ASK SOME OF THE LOCALS ABOUT IT.
GREETINGS.
WHO--?
HE LOOKS FAMILIAR...
I THINK IT'S WATERMAN.
I'M LOOKING FOR A SURFACER'S VESSEL. IT'S CALLED A SUBMARINE--IT LOOKS SOMETHING LIKE A METAL WHALE.
WHO WOULD WANT TO EAT A METAL WHALE?
I DON'T EVEN LIKE WHALE.
WE HAD SOME TASTY TARPON EARLIER!
SO YOU HAVEN'T SEEN IT?
SEEN WHAT?
THE SUBMARINE--THE METAL WHALE!
WHAT METAL WHALE?
WHAT'S A SUBMARINE?
WHAT WERE YOU SAYING?
WAS I SAYING SOMETHING?
DID SOMEONE MENTION TARPON?
MMM, YES--FOOD.
FOOD.
I HONESTLY DON'T KNOW WHY I BOTHER WITH THEM.
COMIC RELIEF?

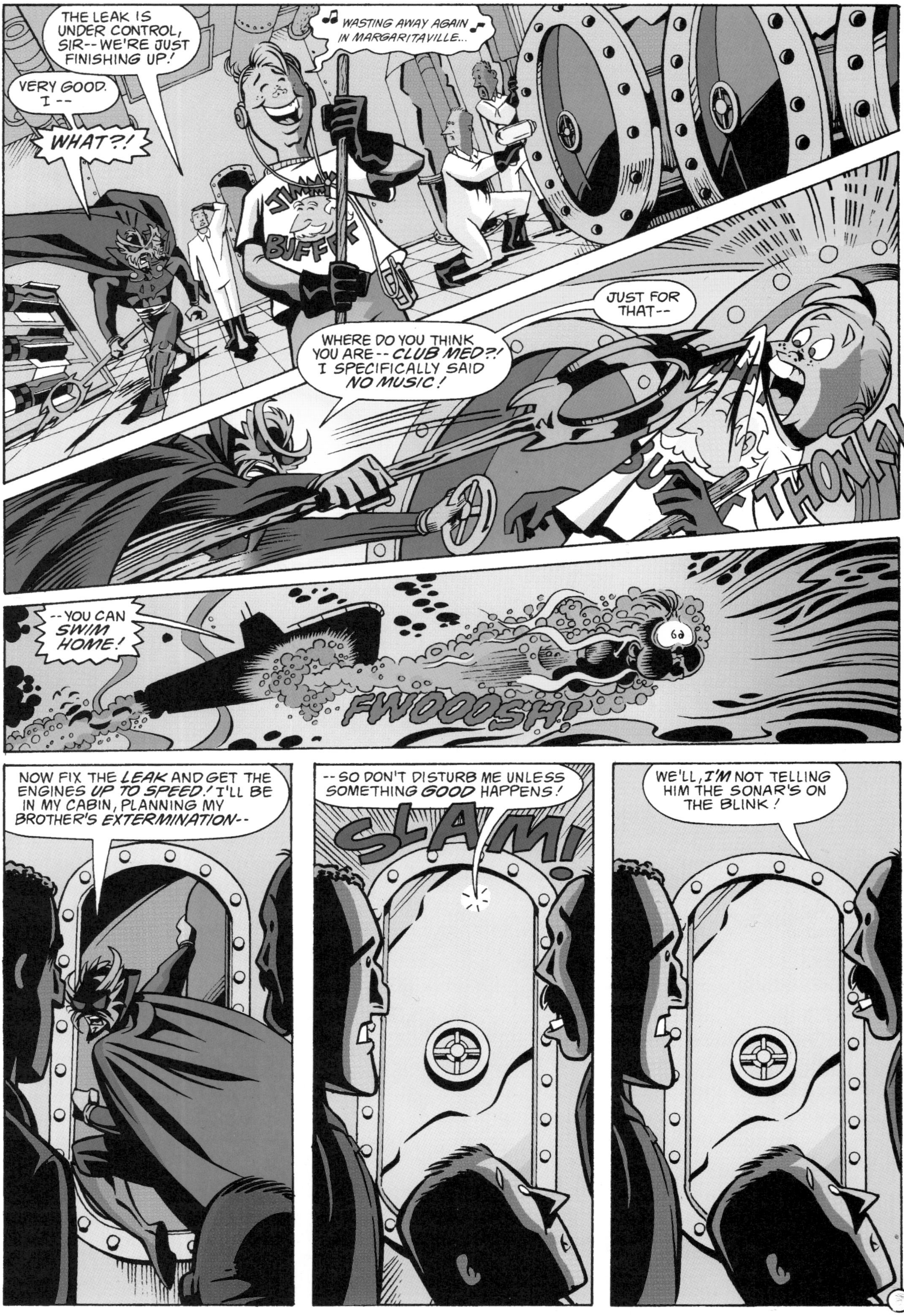

THE LEAK IS UNDER CONTROL, SIR--WE'RE JUST FINISHING UP!
♫ WASTING AWAY AGAIN IN MARGARITAVILLE... ♪
VERY GOOD. I --
WHAT?!
WHERE DO YOU THINK YOU ARE--CLUB MED?! I SPECIFICALLY SAID NO MUSIC!
JUST FOR THAT--
THONK!
--YOU CAN SWIM HOME!
FWOOOSH!

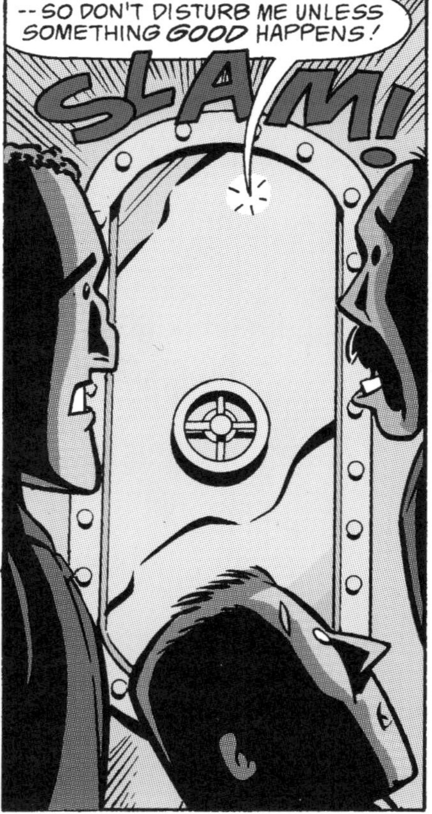

I'VE BEEN WONDERING-- THE DEVICE ON YOUR ARM--IS IT SOME SORT OF DECORATION? TO ATTRACT FEMALES OF YOUR SPECIES, PERHAPS?
I'VE NEVER KNOWN SUCH A CHATTY DOLPHIN. HE MAKES ORM SEEM POSITIVELY LACONIC!
NO--I LOST MY HAND FIGHTING A BEING NAMED CHARYBDIS. HE WAS TRYING TO STEAL MY ABILITY TO COMMUNICATE WITH SEA CREATURES...
KERASH!
I THINK WE'VE FOUND HIM.
THANKS FOR YOUR HELP. BUT FROM HERE ON, I'D BETTER GO ALONE--
"--THIS COULD GET MESSY!"
YOU BLASTED IDIOTS! WHY DIDN'T YOU TELL ME THE SONAR WASN'T WORKING?! WE RAN STRAIGHT INTO THOSE ROCKS!
THAT'S EASY FOR YOU TO SAY--YOU CAN BREATHE UNDERWATER!
DON'T BOTHER WITH THOSE DIVING SUITS --WE'VE GOT MORE IMPORTANT THINGS TO WORRY ABOUT!
PATCH THAT HOLE! LOOK AT ALL THE WATER THAT'S COMING IN!
THAT'S NOT ALL THAT'S COMING IN!
YOU?! NO! NOT NOW! THIS ISN'T FAIR!
I HAVEN'T EVEN BEGUN MY NEXT CAMPAIGN AGAINST YOU! HOW DID YOU FIND ME?
Oh, COME ON, ORM. YOU'RE TALKING TO AQUAMAN, REMEMBER? YOU KNOW, "LIVES UNDERWATER, TALKS TO FISH"?

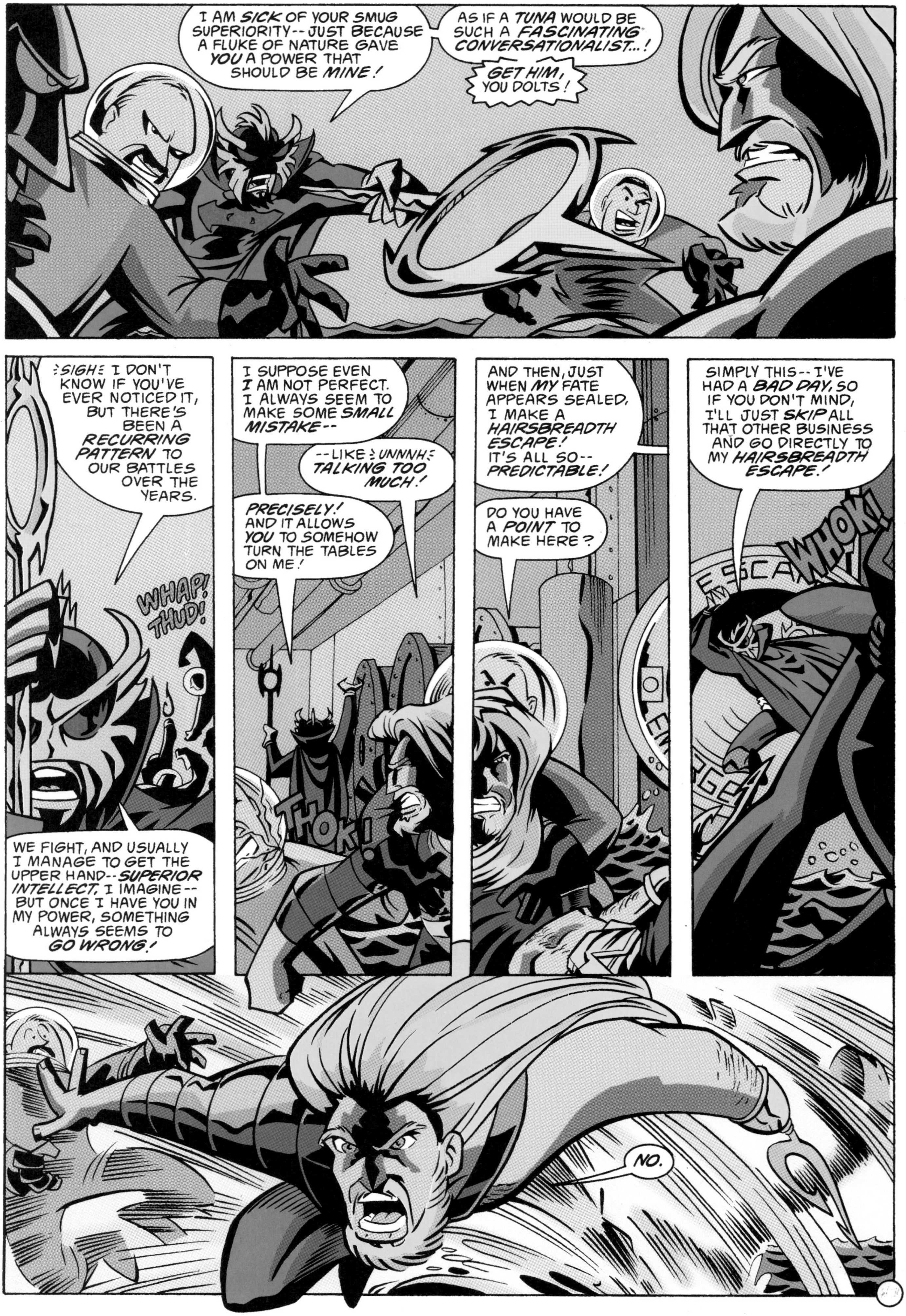

SIGH I DON'T KNOW IF YOU'VE EVER NOTICED IT, BUT THERE'S BEEN A *RECURRING PATTERN* TO OUR BATTLES OVER THE YEARS.

WHAP! THUD!

WE FIGHT, AND USUALLY I MANAGE TO GET THE UPPER HAND-- *SUPERIOR INTELLECT,* I IMAGINE-- BUT ONCE I HAVE YOU IN MY POWER, SOMETHING ALWAYS SEEMS TO *GO WRONG!*

I SUPPOSE EVEN *I* AM NOT PERFECT. I ALWAYS SEEM TO MAKE SOME *SMALL MISTAKE*--

--LIKE *UNNNH* *TALKING TOO MUCH!*

PRECISELY! AND IT ALLOWS *YOU* TO SOMEHOW TURN THE TABLES ON ME!

THOK!

AND THEN, JUST WHEN *MY* FATE APPEARS SEALED, I MAKE A *HAIRSBREADTH ESCAPE!* IT'S ALL SO-- *PREDICTABLE!*

DO YOU HAVE A *POINT* TO MAKE HERE?

SIMPLY THIS-- I'VE HAD A *BAD DAY,* SO IF YOU DON'T MIND, I'LL JUST *SKIP* ALL THAT OTHER BUSINESS AND GO DIRECTLY TO MY *HAIRSBREADTH ESCAPE!*

WHOK!

NO.

I'M *TIRED* OF CHASING YOU, ORM--

--LET'S END THIS *NOW!*
BOK!
ESCAPE

VERY WELL--
ZZZIIKK!
--IF YOU *INSIST!*
SHOOOSH!

HOLD STILL, BLAST YOOOOF!
ah, YES-- ANOTHER EXAMPLE OF YOUR FAMOUS SUPERIOR INTELLECT AT WORK!
THOOMP!
HHUUNF!
ALL RIGHT, ORM! NOW--
NOW WHAT? WHAT ARE YOU GOING TO DO, BROTHER-- KILL ME?
GO AHEAD! YOU WANT TO END THIS-- AND YOU KNOW KILLING ME IS THE ONLY WAY YOU'LL EVER STOP ME!
WHAT'S THE MATTER, SEA KING-- DON'T YOU HAVE THE GUTS?
THAT'S WHAT POWER IS ALL ABOUT-- HAVING THE WILL TO MAKE THE HARD DECISIONS!
YOU DON'T DESERVE YOUR POWER--OR YOUR KINGDOM! YOU'RE TOO WEAK! THIS SIMPLE CHOICE HAS YOU PARALYZED!
UNLESS YOU WANT TO SPEND THE REST OF YOUR LIFE AS MY JAILER, YOU HAVE ONLY TWO CHOICES. YOU CAN KILL ME--
--OR YOU CAN LET ME GO-- AND WE'LL DO THIS ALL OVER AGAIN NEXT TIME!
THERE HAS TO BE ANOTHER WAY, ORM, WE'RE BROTHERS -- WE DON'T HAVE TO FIGHT!
oh, YES-- THERE IS A THIRD OPTION--

--YOU CAN DIE!
WH-CHANG!
I'VE CONCOCTED COUNTLESS ELABORATE SCHEMES TO BRING ABOUT YOUR DEMISE...
--SHUT UP.
YOU DARE--?!
--BUT ENOUGH OF THAT!
MY ARMS ARE PINNED--CAN'T GET LEVERAGE! THIS WILL TAKE A FEW MINUTES--A FEW MINUTES I DON'T HAVE!
KLIK
SAY YOUR PRAYERS TO THE SEA-GODS, BROTHER--
--BUT KEEP THEM SHORT! THOSE TORPEDOES WILL DETONATE IN 20 SECONDS!
HA! I DON'T THINK YOU FULLY APPRECIATE THE IRONY OF THIS SITUATION!
...BUT NOW THAT I'VE FINALLY SUCCEEDED, IT WASN'T DUE TO BRILLIANT PLANNING OR PERFECT EXECUTION-- IT WAS JUST SHEER LUCK! IT'S REALLY--
ORM--

AT LAST! I'M RID OF AQUAMAN FOREVER!
WHOOOSH!
I THOUGHT HE'D NEVER LEAVE! MY ATTEMPT TO PROVOKE HIM NEARLY BACKFIRED-- HE SEEMED READY TO STICK AROUND AND ARGUE RIGHT THROUGH THE EXPLOSION!
I'D BETTER MAKE THIS SHOT GOOD--
--OR IT'LL BE MY LAST!
CHOONK!
MADE IT! NOW I'LL REEL IN THE LINE AND SEE WHICH GIVES FIRST--
-- THE LINE, THIS DEBRIS, OR MY ARM!
AAGGGHH!
KERASH!

CHHOOOOOOM!
WHAT WAS THAT?!
WITH OUR LUCK PROBABLY AN UNDERWATER VOLCANO ERUPTING! NOW SHUT UP AND GET THIS THING GOING!
I'VE RIDDEN BICYCLES THAT WERE MORE COMPLICATED THAN THIS ESCAPE POD! IF YOU CAN'T FIGURE IT OUT, LET ME DRIVE!
NO--
--I'LL DRIVE!
I AM GLAD TO SEE YOU! I FEARED THAT YOU AND HE MIGHT KILL EACH OTHER!
WE DIDN'T MISS BY MUCH! HE BELIEVES OUR CONFLICT MUST END IN DEATH, AND THE ONLY CHOICE WE HAVE IS WHO WILL DIE.
BUT I BELIEVE THERE'S ANOTHER PATH. SOME-DAY...
...I'LL WIN HIM OVER!
THOUGH THE SEVEN SEAS MAY COME BETWEEN US, HE IS MY BROTHER. IT'S LIKE THE SURFACE-DWELLERS SAY...
...BLOOD IS THICKER THAN WATER.
END

SPOT THE DIFFERENCE

Before Batman and Robin leap off into another adventure, say how picture 'B' is different to 'A' in twelve ways!

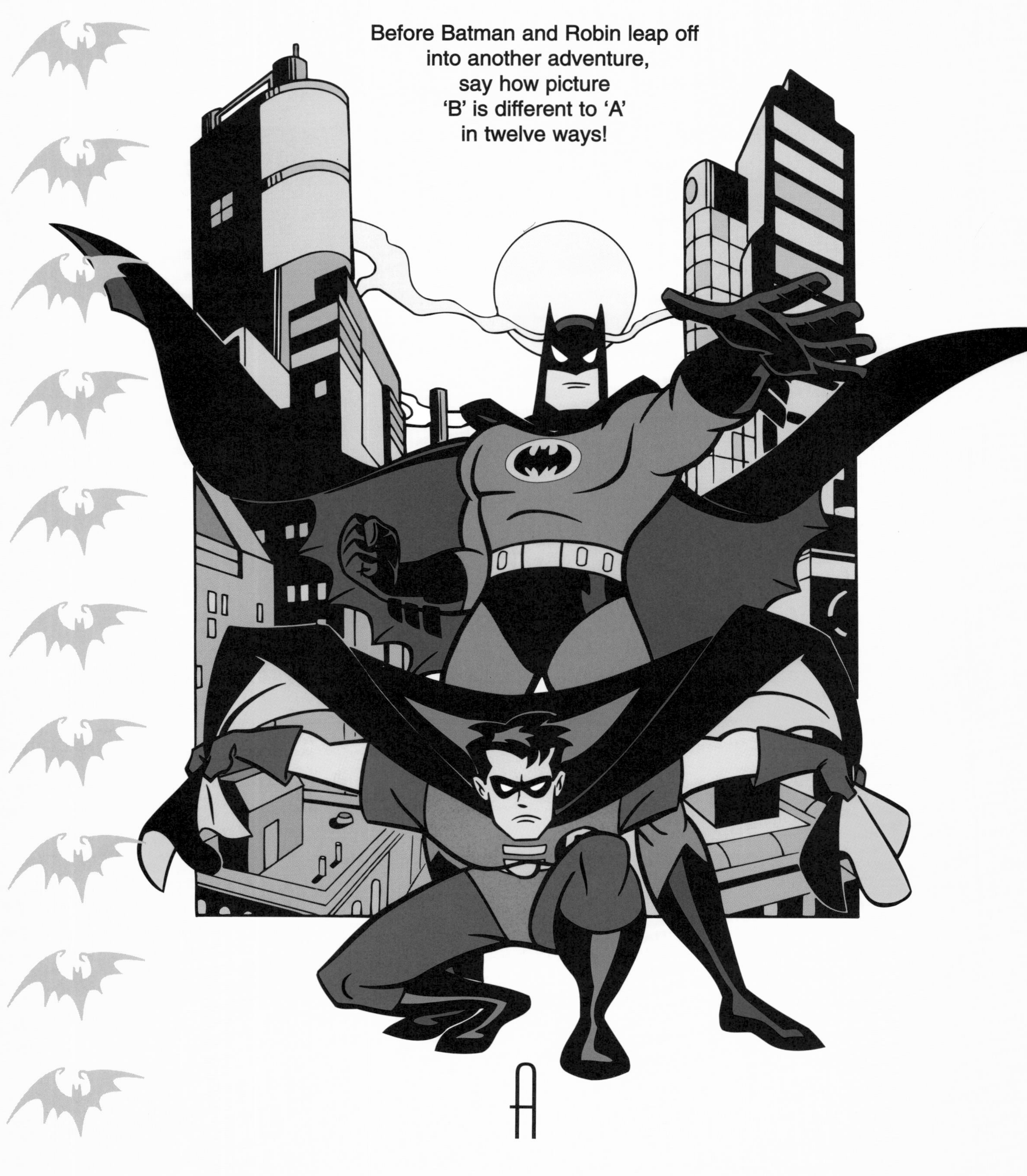

Answer: In 'B', 7 things are missing: Batman's belt buckle; the moon, 2 windows in the builbings to the left; Robin's chest symbol; highlight in Robin's hair and part of Robins cloak.
5 things have been added: Two clouds; a skyscraper; an air-vent on the roof top; a tile on the ledge of the bottom right hand building.

B

ARE YOU A SUPERMAN BUFF?

How much do you know about Superman? Answer these questions, then check your score to see if you're a super-slick Superman sleuth!

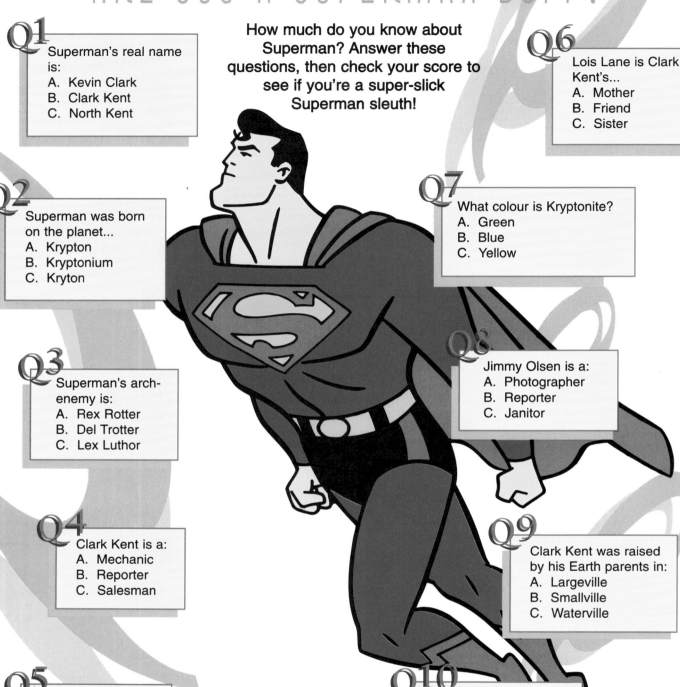

Q1
Superman's real name is:
A. Kevin Clark
B. Clark Kent
C. North Kent

Q2
Superman was born on the planet...
A. Krypton
B. Kryptonium
C. Kryton

Q3
Superman's arch-enemy is:
A. Rex Rotter
B. Del Trotter
C. Lex Luthor

Q4
Clark Kent is a:
A. Mechanic
B. Reporter
C. Salesman

Q5
Clark Kent's best friend is:
A. Johnny Carson
B. Jackie Bosson
C. Jimmy Olsen

Q6
Lois Lane is Clark Kent's...
A. Mother
B. Friend
C. Sister

Q7
What colour is Kryptonite?
A. Green
B. Blue
C. Yellow

Q8
Jimmy Olsen is a:
A. Photographer
B. Reporter
C. Janitor

Q9
Clark Kent was raised by his Earth parents in:
A. Largeville
B. Smallville
C. Waterville

Q10
Clark Kent works at:
A. The *Daily World*
B. The *Daily Globe*
C. The *Daily Planet*

For each correct answer, score 2 points!

SCORE: 0-6 points
Give yourself a big raspberr
you're obviously not a Superman buff!

SCORE: 8-14 POINTS
Not bad, but not a super-score, either!

SCORE: 16-20 POINTS
You really are a super-doop
Superman scorer!

Answers:
1-B. 2-A. 3-C. 4-B. 5-C. 6-B. 7-A.
8-A. 9-B. 10-C.

--YANKEES READY TO START THIS 3-GAME SERIES AGAINST THE RIVAL BALTIMORE ORIOLES.
I GOT FIVE BUCKS SAYS THE YANKS SWEEP!

NO TAKERS? WHASSAMATTER WITH YOU GUYS?
CALM YOURSELF, MY FRIEND! OF COURSE NO ONE HERE BETS AGAINST THE YANKS--THEY ALL ROOT FOR THE HOME TEAM!

DON'T BE SO SURE, RADU!
I'LL BET I CAN FIND SOME ORIOLES FANS HERE...

... STARTING WITH YOU!
uh--uh--uh...

NOW... WHO'S GOING TO WIN THE GAME TONIGHT?
TH-THE ORIOLES...
THE BIRDS'LL SWEEP THE SERIES!
WHY, YOU--
LOUSY TRAITORS --!

GREEN LANTERN

SO THIS LADY WALKS INTO AN ESPRESSO BAR...

OOOF!
HEY! WATCH IT, YOU--!
YEEOW!
ROTTEN DOUBLE-DEALIN' SNAKE!
I'M GONNA--!
SMAK!
KRUNCH
KRAASH!!
TINKLE TINKLE!
BOK!
@#%*!!

STEVE VANCE - WRITER
JOHN DELANEY - PENCILS
RON BOYD - INKS
TIM HARKINS - LETTERS
BOB LE ROSE - COLORS
FRANK BERRIOS - ASS'T EDITS
KC CARLSON - EDITS

HA! THAT'S ONE OF THE THINGS I LOVE ABOUT THIS MUDBALL -- EARTHLINGS ARE SO EASILY PROVOKED!

--SLOW ROLLER UP THE THIRD BASE LINE. RIPKEN CHARGES IT--
Oh, MAN-- NOTHING ON THE RADIO BUT A LAME-O BASEBALL GAME! JUST ANOTHER EXCITING NIGHT IN THE LIFE OF KYLE RAYNER, FREELANCE ARTIST!
I TELL THE ART DIRECTOR I LIKE CARTOONS, AND SHE ASSIGNS ME THIS...

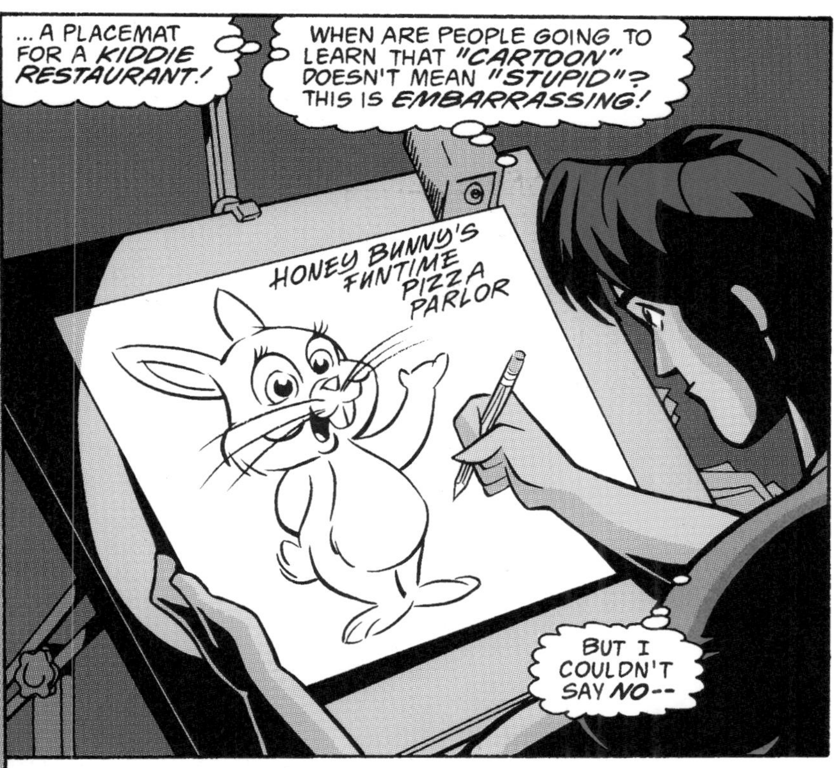

...A PLACEMAT FOR A KIDDIE RESTAURANT!
WHEN ARE PEOPLE GOING TO LEARN THAT "CARTOON" DOESN'T MEAN "STUPID"? THIS IS EMBARRASSING!
HONEY BUNNY'S FUNTIME PIZZA PARLOR
BUT I COULDN'T SAY NO--

--IT'D BE EVEN MORE EMBARRASSING IF THE FIRST OF THE MONTH ROLLED AROUND AND I DIDN'T HAVE THE RENT MONEY FOR RADU!
I'M STARTING TO SEE THIS RABBIT IN MY SLEEP! I'VE ABOUT REACHED THE--
SNAP
--BREAKING POINT?!

MAYBE IT'S TIME TO GO DOWN TO RADU'S FOR A CUP OF--

RRRRRRRRRRR

WHOA! SIRENS-- COPS ARE PULLING UP RIGHT OUTSIDE!

THERE'S A CROWD DOWN THERE.
CAN'T TELL WHAT'S GOING ON, BUT WHAT-EVER IT IS--

--IT'S GOT TO BE MORE INTERESTING THAN HONEY BUNNY!
I'LL CHECK IT OUT--

--AS GREEN LANTERN!
A MINI-RIOT AT THE COFFEE SHOP! LOOKS LIKE SOME OF RADU'S CUSTOMERS HAD BETTER SWITCH TO DECAF!
NEED A HAND, OFFICERS?
YANKEES!
ORIOLES!
CLOONEY!
KILMER!
MACINTOSH!
WINDOWS!
LOOK--GREEN LANTERN!
LET'S GET 'IM!
YEAH!!
Oh, TERRIFIC! WELL, AT LEAST THEY CAN ALL AGREE ON SOMETHING!
THONK!
COME ON!
GET HIM!
NAIL THE BUM!
GET HIM!
YEAH--GET HIM!

GOTTA PUT A STOP TO THIS-- I'LL JUST WHIP UP SOME APPROPRIATE HOLDING CELLS FOR THESE GUYS.
NEVER THOUGHT I'D BE HAPPY TO SEE PEOPLE BEING MUGGED...

NOW MAYBE I CAN GET TO THE BOTTOM OF ALL THIS--
HAHA HAHA HAHA

THANKS, LADY-- I KNOW I'M WITTY, BUT EVEN I DIDN'T THINK I WAS THAT FUNNY!
CURB YOUR INSOLENT TONGUE, MORTAL-- YOU ARE ADDRESSING AN EMISSARY OF THE GREAT LORD DARKSEID!
I AM AMAZING GRACE!

DARKSEID?! SHE WORKS FOR THE BADDEST BAD GUY IN THE UNIVERSE?! WHAT DID I DO TO DESERVE THIS?
"AMAZING GRACE," HUH? SO DOES THAT MEAN HE'S CHUCK?
WHO--?!

GODFREY!
GLORIOUS GODFREY, IF YOU PLEASE, DEAR SISTER--I DO SO PREFER MY FULL NAME!

HOW DARE YOU INTRUDE UPON MY PLANS--
TUT TUT! I ADMIT THAT CURIOSITY LED ME TO FOLLOW YOU HERE FROM OUR HOMEWORLD OF APOKOLIPS--

--AND NOW I DISCERN THE ESSENCE OF YOUR SCHEME TO GAIN FAVOR WITH DARKSEID.

NOT A BAD IDEA-- A SHAME YOU HAVEN'T THE SKILL TO CARRY IT OUT!
UH-OH. I DON'T THINK I LIKE THE WAY THIS BOZO'S LOOKING AT ME...
SORRY TO INTRUDE ON A FAMILY QUARREL, BUT WHAT'S THE DEAL?

I MEAN, IS DARKSEID GOING TO TAKE OVER THE WORLD WITH ESPRESSO BARS? I THOUGHT THAT WAS STARBUCK'S PLAN!
WHY, YOU--
WAIT, GREEN LANTERN--!
6

--I AM NOT YOUR ENEMY--I AM YOUR FRIEND! I CAN HELP YOU SEE THE TRUTH!
LOOK INSIDE YOURSELF--IN YOUR OWN MIND--FOR THAT IS WHERE YOUR TRUE ENEMY DWELLS!
WHAT THE--? FEELS LIKE--HE'S REACHING RIGHT INTO MY BRAIN--!
YES! RELEASE IT--LET YOUR ENEMY COME FORTH!
UNNH--CAN'T--FOCUS MY WILL--TO CONTROL THE RING--
AHH!
THUMP!
MY, MY--THE THINGS ONE FINDS IN A HUMAN'S MIND!

THE POWER RING-- THE LAST ONE IN EXISTENCE! THE ULTIMATE WEAPON, GIVING FORM TO THE WILL OF ITS WEARER--
--HOW EVER DID THE GUARDIANS COME TO BESTOW IT ON THIS LITTLE MAN--?

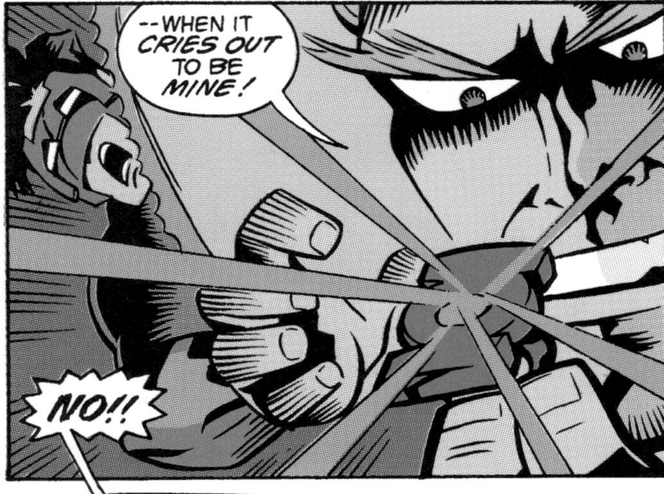
--WHEN IT CRIES OUT TO BE MINE!
NO!!

THIS WAS MY IDEA! THE RING IS RIGHTFULLY MINE!
DON'T GIVE YOURSELF TOO MUCH CREDIT, MY DEAR.

TRUE, YOUR LITTLE DIVERSION AT THE COFFEE SHOP DREW GREEN LANTERN OUT INTO THE OPEN--
--BUT IT WAS I WHO TRAPPED HIM, AND I WHO SHALL WIELD THE RING! YOUR POWERS ARE TOO WEAK FOR SUCH A TASK!

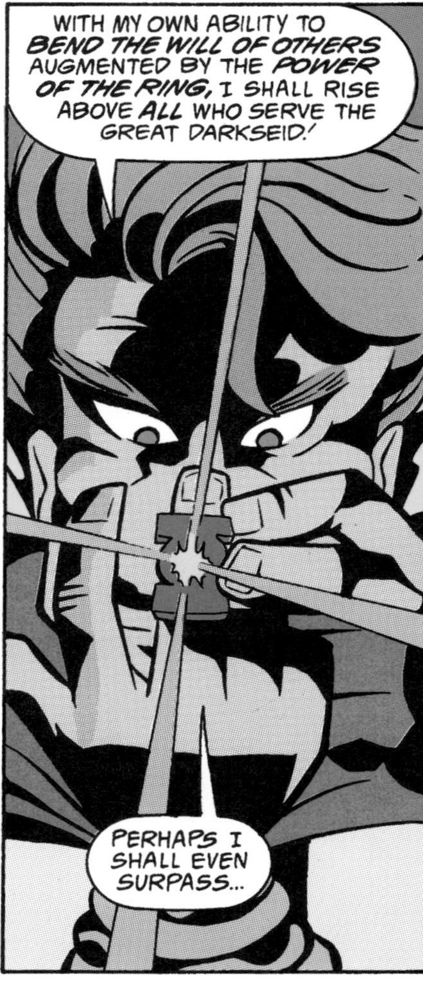
WITH MY OWN ABILITY TO BEND THE WILL OF OTHERS AUGMENTED BY THE POWER OF THE RING, I SHALL RISE ABOVE ALL WHO SERVE THE GREAT DARKSEID!
PERHAPS I SHALL EVEN SURPASS...

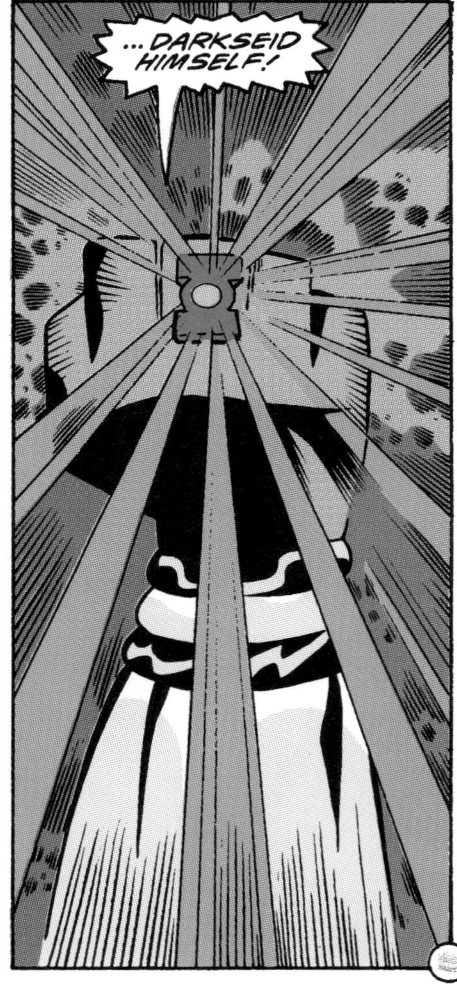
...DARKSEID HIMSELF!

AND NOW...

NOW...

WORK, YOU BLASTED TRINKET! DO SOMETHING!!
HA!
SO GLORIOUS GODFREY WILL CHALLENGE THE POWER OF DARKSEID HIMSELF, WILL HE?

THE ACCURSED *GUARDIANS*, WHO *MADE* THE RING, MUST HAVE DESIGNATED *THIS HUMAN* AS ITS *SOLE USER*!
VERY WELL--

--HE SHALL CONTROL THE RING--AND *I* SHALL *CONTROL HIM*!

WOK!

THAT'S WHAT *YOU THINK*, PAL!

NOW THAT I'VE GOT THAT *BUNNY* OFF MY BACK, I'M GETTING RID OF *YOU TWO*, TOO!

STOP!

RELEASE ME! I AM YOUR FRIEND-- YOUR MASTER!

IT WON'T WORK-- THIS TIME!

NOW WHOSE POWERS ARE TOO WEAK? YOU NEED MY AID, GODFREY--
-- YOU NEED A PARTNER!
AGREED, BLAST IT!

RELEASE US! YOU CANNOT RESIST!
OBEY US! WE ARE YOUR MASTERS!
NO...

YOUR PITIFUL HUMAN BRAIN IS A SWAMP OF UNCERTAINTY AND INSECURITY!
WE WILL CONTROL YOU! WE WILL CLARIFY YOUR MIND.

WE WILL DOMINATE YOU! YOU ARE POWERLESS AGAINST US!

YOU ARE CAUGHT--

"--LIKE A FLY IN AMBER!"
WHAT'S THIS--STILL STRUGGLING? AREN'T YOU GRATEFUL TO US FOR LIFTING THE BURDEN OF DECISION FROM YOU?
YOU WILL LEARN TO SERVE US WELL. BUT FIRST, I THINK IT'S TIME YOU LEARNED A LITTLE HUMILITY!
PUNT!
KRAAASH!
Oh, NO!
LOOK OUT!
HOLY--!
RUN!

CAN'T THINK STRAIGHT! GOT TO--FIND SOMETHING MY MIND CAN--HANG ON TO.!

THE RING--THE LAST POWER RING! GIVEN TO ME--BY THE LAST OF THE GUARDIANS!

ANYTHING I CAN THINK OF--I CAN WILL INTO EXISTENCE --WITH THE RING!

IF I CAN JUST--CONTROL MY WILL!

MORE THAN THE RING--ALL THOSE WHO WORE THE RINGS --BEFORE ME--

--ALAN SCOTT, GUY GARDNER, JOHN STEWART--

--HAL JORDAN.

AND ALL THE ONES I'LL NEVER KNOW --THE WHOLE GREEN LANTERN CORPS--

THEY PATROLLED THE GALAXIES --THEY WERE HEROES, ALL OF THEM--AND NOW--

--I'M THE LAST GREEN LANTERN!

I MAY NOT LIKE BASEBALL, BUT I KNOW HOW TO *FIELD*--
WHAP!

--AND I'LL SHOW DARKSEID'S LITTLE BUDDIES THAT I CAN *HIT*, TOO!
SORRY FOR THE *SCARE*, MA'AM--I'LL MAKE SURE IT DOESN'T HAPPEN *AGAIN*!

ALL RIGHT, YOU TWO! IF YOU LIKED *HONEY BUNNY*, I'VE GOT SOMETHING YOU'RE GOING TO *LOVE*--

--MEET *LI'L GODFREY* AND *BABY GRACE*!
PUT ME *DOWN*, YOU WRETCHED INFANT!

CURSE YOU, GODFREY-- THIS IS ALL *YOUR* FAULT! IF YOU HADN'T *BUTTED IN*--
Oh, *SHUT UP*! IF YOU *MUST* TALK, TELL ME HOW WE'RE GOING TO *ESCAPE*!

A BOOM TUBE! DARKSEID MUST HAVE SENT IT-- TO CARRY US BACK TO APOKOLIPS!
THEN--HE HAS BEEN WATCHING OUR VISIT TO EARTH!
HE KNOWS-- WE HAVE FAILED!
BOOOOOOM!

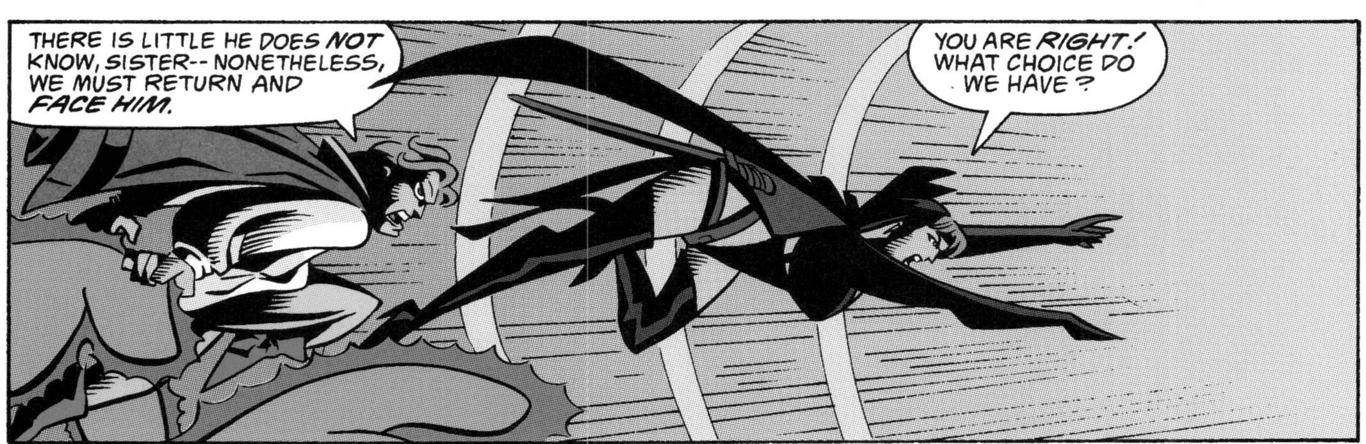
THERE IS LITTLE HE DOES NOT KNOW, SISTER-- NONETHELESS, WE MUST RETURN AND FACE HIM.
YOU ARE RIGHT! WHAT CHOICE DO WE HAVE?

WOW!
BOOOOM!
I SORTA HATED TO LET THEM GO, BUT WHAT THE HECK--
--NOTHING I COULD'VE DONE WITH THOSE TWO WOULD BE AS BAD AS...WELL, WHATEVER DARKSEID HAS IN MIND FOR THEM!

I'D BETTER STOP BY RADU'S ON THE WAY HOME. IT LOOKS LIKE HONEY BUNNY AND I ARE IN FOR A LONG NIGHT--
--AND THAT'S ONE BATTLE WHERE A DOUBLE ESPRESSO WILL BE MORE USEFUL THAN MY POWER RING!
END